DESIGN AND TECHNOLO

RESISTANT MATERIALS
to GCSE

Andy Fair

◆

Nick Rose

OXFORD
UNIVERSITY PRESS

OXFORD

UNIVERSITY PRESS

Great Clarendon Street, Oxford OX2 6DP

Oxford University Press is a department of the University of Oxford.
It furthers the University's objective of excellence in research, scholarship,
and education by publishing worldwide in

Oxford New York

Athens Auckland Bangkok Bogotá Buenos Aires Calcutta
Cape Town Chennai Dar es Salaam Delhi Florence Hong Kong Istanbul
Karachi Kuala Lumpur Madrid Melbourne Mexico City Mumbai
Nairobi Paris São Paulo Singapore Taipei Tokyo Toronto Warsaw
with associated companies in Berlin Ibadan

Oxford is a registered trade mark of Oxford University Press

in the UK and in certain other countries

Database right Oxford University Press (maker)

First published 2000

British Library Cataloguing in Publication Data

Data available

ISBN 0 19 832790 0

Typeset by Advance Typesetting
Printed in Italy

Introduction

This book has been written for students working towards GCSE Design and Technology: Resistant Materials. All GCSE syllabuses have been considered and the book provides a comprehensive guide to:
- using the design process in coursework
- the working properties of resistant materials and the processes used to manufacture products in the school workshops and manufacturing industry
- the day-to-day work of designers.

The book covers a range of traditional and modern materials in detail, which will help you in your understanding of resistant materials and product design. Topics are set out in double page spreads, each starting with a clear set of objectives, and grouped in chapters in a logical sequence to help you follow the GCSE course.

Questions are provided on each spread to test your knowledge and understanding. These are at both foundation and higher level. Higher level questions have numbers appearing like this **2**

The design of new products using Resistant Materials is something that affects all our lives and can be creative, exciting and rewarding. The modern designer uses traditional and modern materials and new technologies to design and manufacture products that are fit for purpose, environmentally sound, and pleasing to look at. The book includes examples of modern design processes, products and designers.

Use this book to help you create and develop your own products and to complement your studies of Resistant Materials.

Andy Fair   Nick Rose

Contents

Designing

ANALYSIS AND DESIGN

1.1 Problem analysis   6
1.2 Product research   8
1.3 Writing a specification   10
1.4 Design ideas   12
1.5 Developing your idea   14
1.6 Modelling your idea   16
1.7 Presenting final plans   18
1.8 Manufacturing in quantity   20
1.9 Plan for manufacture   22
1.10 Product evaluation   24

SELECTION AND TEST

2.1 Selection of materials   26
2.2 Materials testing for suitability   28

Making

WORKING WITH WOOD

3.1 Preparing wood for use   30
3.2 Choosing and marking out wood   32
3.3 Hand tools for cutting wood   34
3.4 Power tools for cutting wood   36
3.5 Shaping wood   38
3.6 Forming wood   40
3.7 Joining wood: carcases   42
3.8 Joining wood: framework   44
3.9 Specialised wood joints   46
3.10 Adhesives and fixings   48
3.11 Wood manufacturing in quantity   50
3.12 Finishing woodwork   52

WORKING WITH METAL

4.1 Choosing and preparing metals   54
4.2 Marking out metals   56
4.3 Cutting and drilling metals   58
4.4 Turning and milling metals   60
4.5 Metal shaping and forming   62
4.6 Pressing and die-casting metal   64
4.7 Forging and sand-casting   66
4.8 Joining metals   68
4.9 Threading and riveting metal   70
4.10 Soldering and brazing   72
4.11 Metal manufacturing in quantity   74
4.12 Heat treatment of metals   76
4.13 Finishing metals   78

WORKING WITH PLASTICS

5.1	Choosing and marking out on plastics	80
5.2	Cutting out plastics	82
5.3	Shaping and forming plastics (I)	84
5.4	Shaping and forming plastics (II)	86
5.5	Joining plastics	88
5.6	Plastic manufacturing in quantity	90
5.7	Finishing plastic products	92

WIDER ISSUES

6.1	Combining metals	94
6.2	Disassembling familiar objects	96
6.3	Quality control	98
6.4	Production stages	100
6.5	Quality considerations	102

Knowledge and understanding

SYSTEMS

7.1	Systems and control	104
7.2	Mechanical systems	106
7.3	Gears	108
7.4	Levers and pulleys	110
7.5	Computer-aided design	112
7.6	Computer-aided manufacture	114
7.7	Designing control systems	116

HEALTH AND SAFETY

8.1	Recognising hazards in products	118
8.2	Safety at work	120

Appendix: Ergonomic and product data	122
Glossary	124
Index	126
Acknowledgements	128

1.1 Problem Analysis

By the end of this spread, you should be able to:

- understand why designers design new products
- recognise how a designer analyses a problem

Why do we design new products?

As designers, we design new products for a number of reasons.

- There is a need for a new product to **solve a new problem**: look in newspapers, magazines and ask adults for new problems in everyday life or choose one associated with your particular interests.
- There is a need to **improve the performance** of an existing product: a product functions poorly, looks old fashioned, is unreliable.
- There is a need to **redesign a product** because a new technology or innovation has been introduced: new energy source, new video game, new material.
- A company has decided to re-invent a product to **improve the sales**: transparent casing, improved graphics, fashionable colour, attractive wrapper.

You can use these reasons to help you arrive at a **design need**.

What product do you want to design or redesign?

Using any of the above reasons, brainstorm ideas for your design project. Write them down **quickly** on a large sheet of paper as in the diagram.

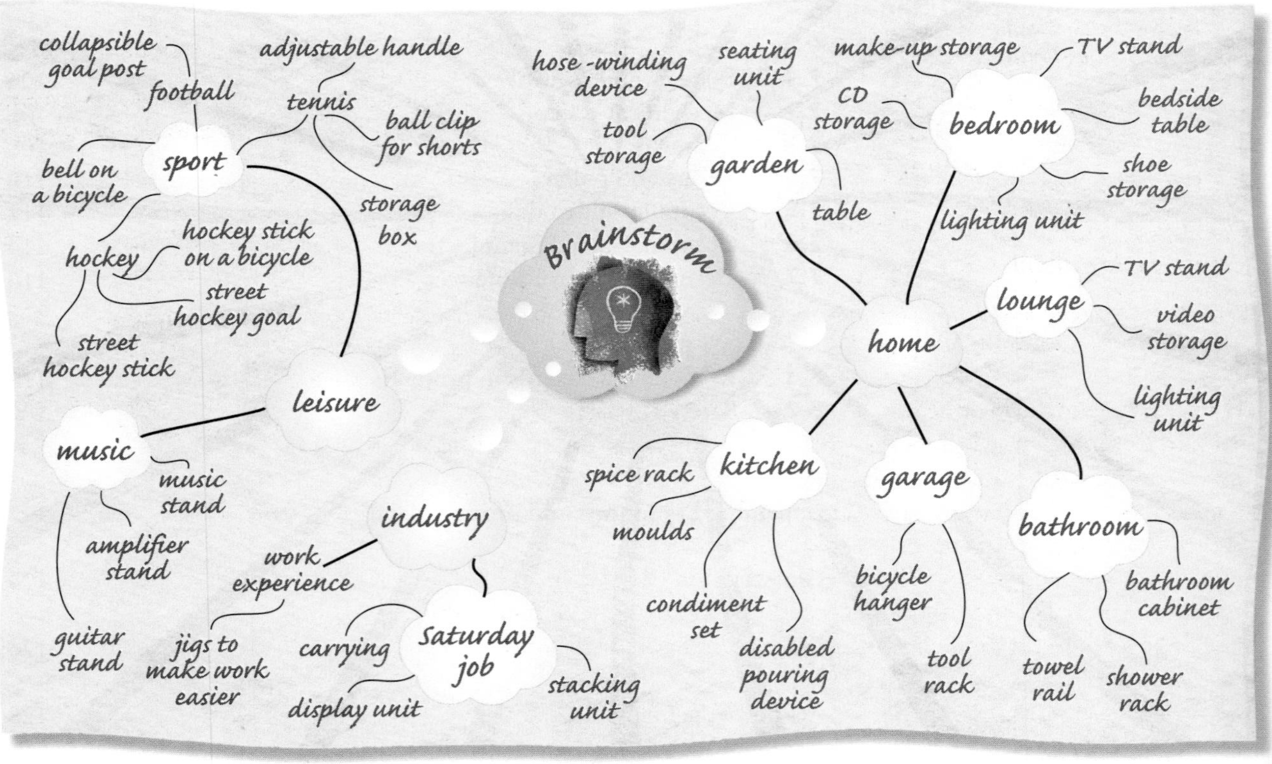

You could also add in products to do with schools, shops, social services, health care, church and community, etc.

Now that you have some ideas for a design project you can begin to analyse these ideas to establish how good they are in order to prepare a **design brief**. To enable you to prepare a design brief you will need to do an **analysis** of the problem that has resulted in a design need for a new, improved or redesigned product.

Analysis

What exactly is a **design problem**? A problem occurs when an existing product does not meet a new need or when no product exists at all. A designer must fully understand all aspects of the need to be able to design a worthwhile product. For example if a designer was given the problem of transporting heavy items on a bicycle the following suggestions could be asked as part of the problem analysis:

- ☐ WHO does the problem affect? (The user of the bicycle, other road users, the owners of the item being carried.)
- ☐ WHAT happens to the bicycle and the load? (Observations of the user under certain conditions.)
- ☐ WHEN is the problem caused? (Time of day, type of work being done, distance involved, etc.)
- ☐ WHY does it cause a problem? (An analysis of the structures and mechanisms on the bicycle for carrying loads and the control exerted by the user. Effect of weather; other road users; time available for task.)

Now look at the questions that were asked to help analyse the need for a new type of high chair for toddlers.

What is the design problem?

Where does the problem occur?

Who does it affect?

What type of solution do you expect to design?

What environment will your design be used in?

Design brief – a high chair for toddlers

Many young children of toddler age like to sit at the dining table with their families. Parents find this difficult when the child is too big for a high chair and yet too small for the family's dining chairs. There is a need for a toddler seating system that can be used at a dining table.

Design and make a seating system that can be used at a dining table and enables children to sit and eat comfortably from the dining table.

The design will be aimed at 3–5 year old children, be attractive, fun, safe to use, durable, easily stored and portable.

When and how often?

What need arises from the stated problem?

Who will use your design?

How will your design be used?

What conditions must apply?

How can I make the product appeal to a wide range of users?

To find out whether a product is worth developing, a company will do **market research** to find out information. This may be in the form of a **questionnaire** or **observation** of users of similar products.

When a company decides they have **confirmed a need** for a new or improved product they can write the design brief to be given to the **design team**. When you have established a design problem that has resulted in a need you can begin to prepare your own design brief for your product.

1 Look at the brainstorm opposite and identify one product idea for each of the three branches of the diagram. Write down WHO the problem affects, WHAT happens when things go wrong, WHEN the problem occurs and WHY it happens.

2 Formulate a design brief for one of the products identified in the brainstorm. Make sure a design team (who may not know you) will understand your design brief.

1.2 PRODUCT RESEARCH

- identify why product research is important
- plan your product research
- present your research report

Planning for success

Thorough **research** before designing and during the design and development of a product is crucial to its success. In industry large amounts of money are spent on research and development (R&D) ensuring the design team answer the following questions:

- ☐ Is there a need for the product?
- ☐ Who will be the user(s) of the product?
- ☐ Are the needs of the user of the product accurately identified?
- ☐ Is there a large enough **market** for the product?
- ☐ What user **environment** will the product be used in?
- ☐ What similar products are already on the market?
- ☐ What is the user's opinion of a good product and a poor product in this market?

Note: 'Market' means all the users who might buy your product. 'Environment' means all the situations, conditions, places, times and circumstances your product might be used in or have to compete in.

You can use these questions to plan your product research. An example **research questionnaire** is given below.

Research Questionnaire for a Toddler's high chair

For my major project in Design and Technology I am designing and making a modern high chair for 3–5 year old children.

1 Have you got any young children?
☐ Yes ☐ No

2 What age are they?
☐ 0–5 ☐ 5–10 ☐ 10–15 years

3 Do you or did you use a high chair when they were younger?
☐ Yes ☐ No

4 What did you use the high chair for?
☐ Feeding ☐ Playing ☐ To keep them under control
☐ Other . . . .

5 Were you happy with the high chair you had bought?
☐ Yes ☐ No

6 What improvements would you have included in the design?
☐ Different colour ☐ Different size ☐ Increased durability
☐ Ease of cleaning ☐ More features ☐ A themed design (e.g. Disney, Chipmunks)

7 Where did you use the high chair?
☐ Lounge ☐ Dining room ☐ Kitchen
☐ Outside ☐ On holiday

8 Would you want the high chair to complement a range of furniture?
☐ Yes ☐ No

9 How much would you be willing to pay for a high chair?
☐ £0–25 ☐ £25–50 ☐ £50–100

10 Would you want the high chair to convert into a low chair?
☐ Yes ☐ No

11 Where did you buy your high chair?
. . . .

Thank you for answering my questions. Your comments have been very useful.

Your **presentation** of the results of this research is very important. Experiment with different **media** to display your research.

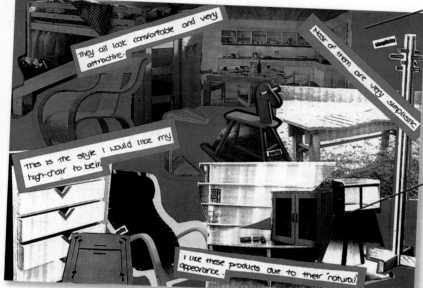

A mood board showing existing similar products will assist the design team.

Photographs of the context of the problem for which you are designing a solution.

Written text of an interview you have had with a prospective user of your product.

Interview with young mother at Toddler Surgery.

When our children were small we used to use the high chair all the time for feeding and playing. The children were playing with simple jigsaw puzzles and artwork.

Our high chair was made using chrome tubing and a blue plastic tray and plastic covered chair. I think it had teddy bears printed on it. It was quite durable but was not easy to clean, and had lots of corners to push wet biscuits into ! I would have liked it to be more stylish as it didn't really suit our furniture. We often used it as a separate chair.

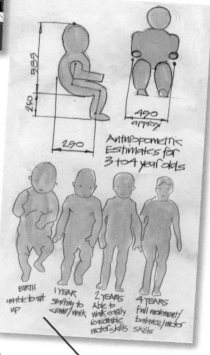

Collect anthropometric data on prospective users of your product in typical application(s).

1 Choose a product that you are making in Design and Technology and make a **research plan** that identifies where and how you will find answers to your research and what you expect to find.

2 Identify a product that you feel has failed because of a lack of research and identify how the problem could have been overcome.

3 Produce a product mood board for an existing household appliance of your choice.

1.3 WRITING A SPECIFICATION

- understand how to construct a design specification

What will the design team need?

In industry designers will often be given a **design brief** by a client which will enable them to carry out further extensive analysis and research. From this they will then be able to establish a **design specification** that will guide the design team during the product's development.

The iMac computer designed by Apple is a good example of an innovative design response to a precise specification and design brief. The brief was to create a product as integrated, simple and small as possible which could be sold at a price suitable for the home computer market. The design incorporates a refreshing use of materials: the case, keyboard and mouse are a mixture of white, translucent, and clear plastic materials. The design is also functional: the case incorporates a carring handle, and a height-adjustable, space-efficient keyboard.

Preparing a specification

A specification is a list of your product's main design **qualities** and **functions**. Where possible the designer puts numerical or physical values to those qualities. For example, below is a list of questions that students have asked themselves in order to prepare a specification for their design task.

Product Designing and making a carrying system for in-line skates.

What are the numerical and physical features? weight, height, length and depth of skates: sizes 3–12? size of spare space required? extra protection required? extra support required? rigid or soft material? durability? carrying handles or straps? fasteners?

Who is going to use my product? The product is going to be designed to appeal to young people aged 10–18 years.

What are the user's physical characteristics? The product's users are young and often physically fit. Anthropometric data will be needed for this age group.

What items must my project contain? The product must contain one pair of in-line skates in varying sizes. It would be an advantage if it could also carry waxes and protective gear.

How important is appearance? The carrying system must appeal to young people and be representative of current fashion styles.

What are the environmental conditions in which my product will be used?
It will be stored indoors but mainly used outdoors. The product may be carried on public transport.

What is the budget I have to work to?
The cost of the product must not be more than £25 for a long-life or £5 for a short-life product.

Are there any specific safety or legal requirements with which my product must comply?
The carrying system could incorporate safety reflective materials for night use.

Are there any restrictions on the use of materials or other resources?
All materials used in the manufacture of the product must be readily available and the product must be made in the school workshops.

How many products am I going to make?
Your specification must take account of manufacturing the product in quantity.
I am going to make a one-off prototype but I will produce templates and jigs that will allow the product to be made in quantity in a school/college situation.

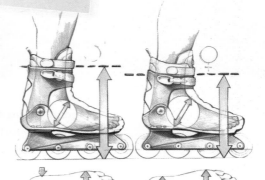

This specification will be used throughout your project to guide creative thinking through design, development, manufacture and evaluation.

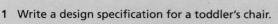

1 Write a design specification for a toddler's chair.

2 Adapt the specification to suit the child
   a) from 0–2 years b) 2–5 years c) 5–8 years.

1.4 DESIGN IDEAS

- present your own design ideas
- annotate your design drawings

How do you start a design or redesign?

Assume you now have a design brief and a design specification with drawings and pictures and questionnaire results. This is when your own ideas and creativity start.

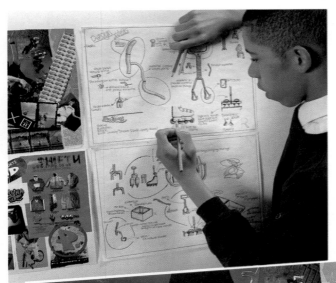

Design ideas

Many designers start this process by surrounding themselves with **images** that are related to the product they are designing to influence their work.

When you are first putting your ideas down onto paper it will be a good idea to look back at your design brief and specification. Sometimes it is useful to come up with ideas for each aspect of your brief or specification, although some criteria can be grouped together under one heading. For example, a student has decided to design and make an in-line skate carrying system. You will notice that the ideas can be separated into different features: carrying by hand, fixing skates to carrying system, add-on features, adjusting, locking, etc.

Presentation of design ideas

The most important feature of your presentation is that it should be easy to understand and show your **creative thinking**. Add notes to your drawings that make reference to materials, textures, functions and values of your product. Designers call these notes **annotation**. Imagine you are going to send your ideas on to another designer and won't be able to speak to them to explain their meaning. Add colour and texture to your drawings to highlight materials. Provide simple sketches of the overall **concept** and detailed drawings of certain **key feature**s.

Do not be worried about putting ideas down on paper quickly and using rough sketches. These drawings are representative of your thinking process and can never be repeated by copying out neatly. You can always sharpen

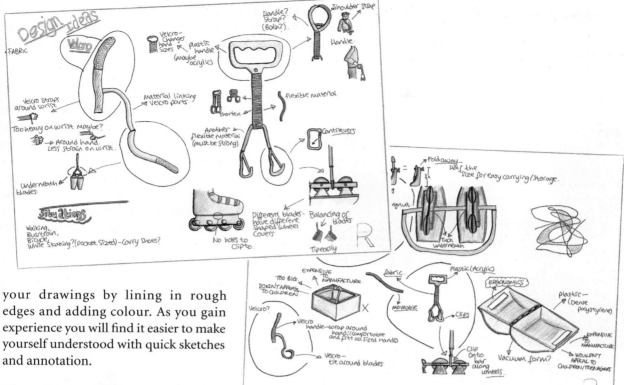

your drawings by lining in rough edges and adding colour. As you gain experience you will find it easier to make yourself understood with quick sketches and annotation.

Choosing a design

After you have produced a wide variety of design ideas you will need to evaluate them, make a shortlist, and then choose one idea to develop further. There are a number of methods that you can use for **design evaluation**.

Look at your specification again and ensure your designs meet all the criteria. This can be made more accurate by producing a chart that gives each part of your design numerical value. This is called **attributes analysis**. You could also ask a likely user of your product what they think of your designs and record their comments. This is called **user evaluation**.

Now record which design idea you have chosen and state the reasons why. Write down what features you may need to develop further.

ATTRIBUTES ANALYSIS

	DESIGN 1	DESIGN 2	DESIGN 3
Attractive	✔✔✔✔○	✔✔✔○○	✔✔✔✔✔
Fun	✔✔✔○○	✔✔✔○○	✔○○○○
Durable	✔✔✔✔✔	✔✔○○○	✔✔✔○○
Simple to use	✔○○○○	✔✔✔✔○	✔✔○○○

1 What do we mean by annotation of design drawings?

2 Produce annotated design drawings for a clock that will be a focal point in a record store, nightclub or dental surgery.

1.5 DEVELOPING YOUR IDEA

- develop your own design idea
- analyse your ideas in terms of form and function

Product development

When you have completed your attributes analysis and user evaluation you should be able to select your preferred design. Do this by crossing the other designs off your shortlist, one at a time, stating alongside why you have done this. Keep your shortlist and notes in case you have to change your mind over the selection you have made.

After you have chosen your design idea you will need to develop it further. Continue to produce design sketches and annotation in more detail. You will have to do some further research in order to design a product that meets the exact needs of your specification. A final evaluation or test will have to be made to check your design against the specification and intended purpose stated in the design brief. This is called assessing the **fitness for purpose**.

FORM
- consider different ideas for base profile
- does it match other products?
- what different colours could be used?

FUNCTION
- will it hold many items?
- is it stable?
- will points on base scratch surfaces?
- does it need a back?

STORAGE SPACE

Form and function

The following questions on form and function may help you with the development of your product. You can prepare a **design checklist** from these questions specially for your own product.

Form

- ☐ How can you visually improve your product?
- ☐ Does the shape complement the context that it will be used in? For example, if you have a very modern hi-tech bedroom does the CD holder that you may be designing complement that context?
- ☐ How could you match its appearance to the hi-fi that it sits alongside and what colour should it be?
- ☐ If your home has a very traditional interior does the product that you have designed complement that room?
- ☐ Is there any traditional detail or material that you could incorporate in your design?
- ☐ Can you add colour, texture or detail to improve its appearance?

Function

☐ Is the product you have designed fit for the purpose?
☐ How can you develop the different functions of the product?
☐ How can you make it moveable, lockable, hinged, folding, waterproof, portable, etc.?

Choice of materials

You now need to match materials up to the specification of the product and the final idea that you have developed (refer to Spread 2.1). Consider a number of materials and then evaluate them against your brief, specification and final design. For example, if you were designing a tool box for a radio-controlled car, evaluate the material under the following headings:

☐ **Construction** – is the material suitable for the construction method?
☐ **Function** – will it soak up moisture?
☐ **Toughness** – what would happen if it was dropped or knocked?
☐ **Strength** – will it be able to carry heavy items?
☐ **Durability** – will it warp or chip?
☐ **Cost** – will it be too expensive?
☐ **Appearance** – colour, finish?

Shaping and joining

Your choice of material has to be considered in conjunction with your construction method and types of joints, hinges, fasteners, clips, etc. Shaping and joining metal, plastic or wood requires very different methods which will influence the design and final performance. Time now to reconsider your choice of design!

Look back at your final design idea and consider what **joining methods** you are going to use to construct your product and evaluate them regarding appearance, strength and other attributes.

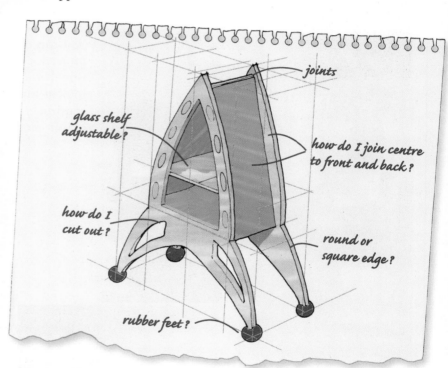

Produce an **outline drawing** of your product. Highlight the points where you need to consider different jointing, folding, closing and securing methods.

---

1 Suggest materials that are suitable for making an outdoor picnic bench and give your reasons why. Ask for relevant leaflets from local nature groups and environmental agencies.

2 Produce your own diagram for a storage container for a collection of games.

1.6 MODELLING YOUR IDEA

Designers use models during different stages of the design process to test their ideas. You may choose to make a model of all or part of your design. You should always have a clear idea about what aspect of your product you aim to test, for example, size, stability, or attractiveness. Materials used for models are cheap and easy to construct. They don't have to be strong or attractive.

Modelling is particularly useful when the product has a shape or form that is difficult to draw, for example a computer mouse. In this example the designer can quickly change the shape of the mouse and ask for an evaluation from fellow designers, or clients and users.

Trialling a concept model for a mouse

You can use modelling techniques in your own projects. For example, if you were making a chair it would be a good idea to start modelling your ideas to look at form, function, stability and methods of construction. To record these ideas take photographs of your models and evaluate their success.

Modelling a high chair using cardboard

Adjusting the design

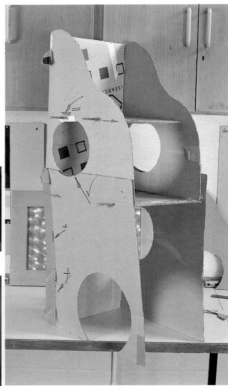

Highlighting key areas for development

MODELLING MATERIALS			
	BOXES	FRAMEWORKS	HANDLES	ORGANIC SHAPES
Paper	✓			
Card	✓	✓		
Corrugated card	✓	✓		
MDF			✓	✓
Wire		✓	✓	
Pipe cleaners		✓		
Foam			✓	✓
Clay			✓	✓
Balsa wood	✓	✓	✓	✓
	TEMPLATES	CHAIRS/TABLES	STORAGE UNITS	FORGING WORK
Paper			✓	
Card	✓	✓	✓	
Corrugated card		✓	✓	
Plywood	✓			
Wire		✓		✓
Pipe cleaners		✓		✓
Balsa wood	✓	✓	✓	✓

1 Produce a model of a bedside lighting unit for a 5–9 year old.

2 What are the advantages of modelling products before manufacture?

1.7 PRESENTING FINAL PLANS

- present your final idea in such a way that the product you have designed can be visualised and made from your working drawing

When you have finished developing and modelling your chosen design idea you will need to produce drawings that enable a manufacturer or client to visualise the product and make a prototype from your drawings.

The drawing or visual presentation could be produced using different techniques. For example: pictorial drawing in **isometric**, **oblique** or **perspective** views or an **orthographic presentation**.

Pictorial drawings (projections)

Oblique

Isometric

Perspective

Orthographic

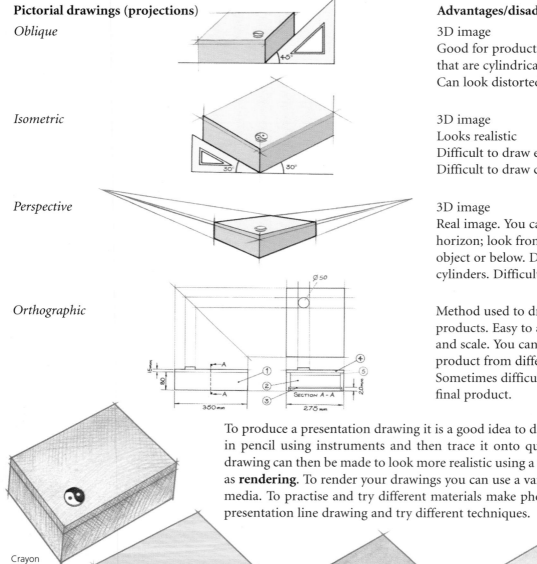

Advantages/disadvantages

3D image
Good for products
that are cylindrical
Can look distorted

3D image
Looks realistic
Difficult to draw ellipses
Difficult to draw curves

3D image
Real image. You can change horizon; look from above an object or below. Difficult to draw cylinders. Difficult to draw curves.

Method used to draw complex products. Easy to add dimensions and scale. You can look at a product from different directions. Sometimes difficult to visualise final product.

To produce a presentation drawing it is a good idea to draw your product in pencil using instruments and then trace it onto quality paper. This drawing can then be made to look more realistic using a technique known as **rendering**. To render your drawings you can use a variety of colouring media. To practise and try different materials make photocopies of your presentation line drawing and try different techniques.

Crayon

Marker

Pastels

Watercolour

Exploded drawings

To simplify methods of construction and assembly it is often useful to produce an **exploded view** of your product. From this view we are able to identify different parts, materials and components. The separate pieces that make up a product are 'exploded' on what we call **lines of action**.

Working drawings

All design studios or teams will produce a working drawing from a visual drawing or model that they have created. The working drawing should enable someone to manufacture your product so it must give lots of information including dimensions and numbered parts.

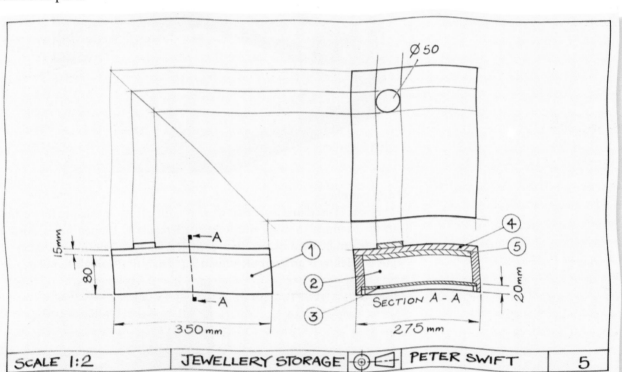

1 If you were designing a desk tidy that was made up of a number of cylindrical objects what presentation drawing method would you use?

2 If you were drawing a watch, how would you give the right impression of the finish?

1.8 MANUFACTURING IN QUANTITY

- understand the need to produce products in quantity
- describe the use of jigs and templates to aid production
- understand why a prototype is made

Production aids

Most designers work on products which will eventually be made in large quantities in factories. They need to ensure that their designs can be **mass produced** in a way which gives consistent results. During your design project you will need to consider methods of producing your products in quantity. Even if you make only the prototype of your design (see opposite) you need to plan how you would ensure accuracy and consistency if your product was being made in quantity. **Jigs** and **templates** are two of the tools used to do this.

Using jigs

A jig is used to ensure that dimensions are maintained accurately and consistently; for example to drill a series of holes at the end of a storage unit.

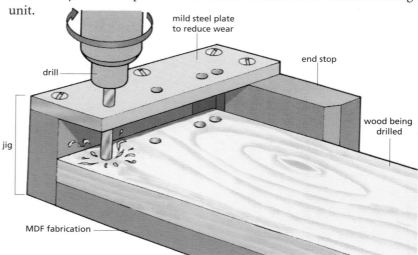

Using templates

A template is used to ensure that we mark out consistent shapes for cutting out; for example to mark out joints or irregularly shaped holes. Also, a template can be used to **tessellate** complex shapes to minimise wastage of material. Below is an example of pattern generation using a template.

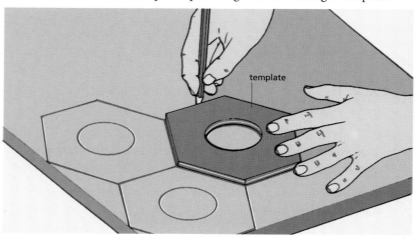

Making and using a prototype

A **prototype** is made from the materials to be used in the final product using similar processes. This means that when the prototype sample is evaluated by the designer and by the client, **feedback** of realistic test results can be provided for any last minute changes required.

The example below shows how a designer has produced a prototype of a recumbent bicycle. The designer has first temporarily held the bicycle together using tape to check dimensions and layout. He has then trialled the handling and manoeuvrability of the bicycle before producing a highly finished prototype.

When you have made a prototype of your product you will need to analyse how aspects of your project can be produced in quantity and to identify which components can be purchased from outside your workshop.

First assembly of a prototype

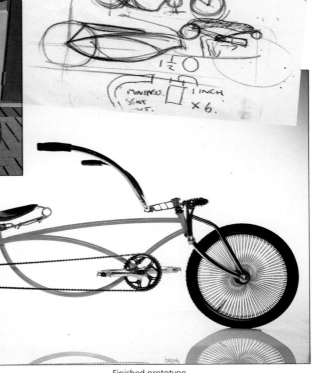

Finished prototype

1 Produce a template for a personal logo that could be used to produce a graphic on your design sheets.

2 How does a manufacturing jig improve the quality of a finished product?

3 Design a manufacturing jig that will be used to drill a wooden pencil holder to contain 10 pencils.

1.9 PLANNING FOR MANUFACTURE

- understand why designers plan the manufacturing process
- understand working drawings and cutting lists
- plan the manufacturing process

Working to a schedule

To ensure that the manufacture of your product is carried out punctually, accurately and without wastage you will need to plan the process carefully. Use a **flow chart** to plan each stage of the manufacture of your product (see Spread 7.1). This is called a **planning schedule**.

Working drawing

The working drawing of the product must show dimensions, separate parts and assembly. It should include any changes resulting from feedback after prototype evaluation.

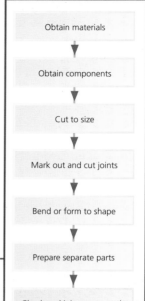

Planning schedule

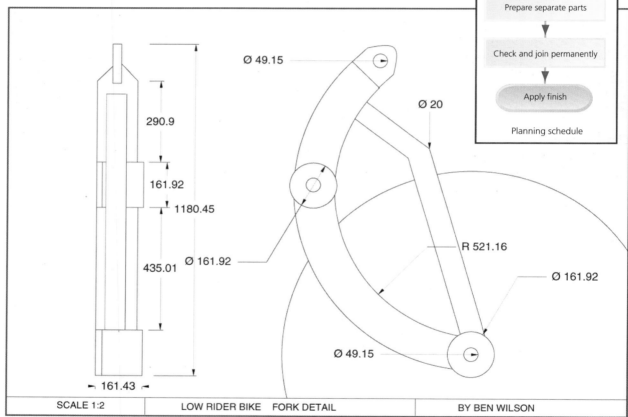

| SCALE 1:2 | LOW RIDER BIKE   FORK DETAIL | BY BEN WILSON |

Cutting list

Has a cutting list been produced that states the description, size and material of each part of your product? This is important for production. If quantities, supplies and costs are included, it is useful for ordering parts. Don't forget to include items to help the assembly stage such as adhesive, tape, screws and paint. These are known as **consumables** used in the course of manufacture.

CUTTING LIST FOR FORK CONFIGURATION AND MATERIAL REQUIREMENTS								
ITEM	DESCRIPTION	NO. OFF	LENGHTH	WIDTH	THICKNESS	MATERIAL	SUPPLIER	UNIT COST
1	Spring	1	100	50	6	Steel	L.R.B	£5.00
2	Damper	1	10	30	15	Rubber	L.R.B.	£0.50
3	Spring bolt	1	130	10	10	Steel	L.R.B.	£1.00
4	Fork crown	1	40	40	6	Steel	L.R.B.	£5.00
5	Goose neck	1	80	100	50	Steel	L.R.B.	£5.00
6	Steer tube	1	300	10	28	Steel	L.R.B.	£8.00
7	Top bolts	2	20	8	8	Steel	BC. Eng	£1.50
8	Fork blades	2	1180	30	30	Steel	Downlow	£10.00
9	Pivot section	4	30	30	30	Steel	Downlow	£2.00
10	Pivot plate	4	30	30	2	Steel	BC. Eng	£0.30
11	Pivot axel	1	150	12	12	Steel	All.G	£3.00

Planning ahead

- Will you require particular materials or components that will need to be ordered? For example the saddle, gears, etc.
- Have you planned how you are going to cut up large materials to avoid **wastage**?
- Do you need to design and make any **jigs** or **templates** that will help you manufacture the product?

Time schedule

You now need to estimate how long each task is going to take and then put the tasks in the order which gives the most efficient use of time. You will need to identify which parts will take the longest to make and so have to be made early in the **production cycle** so that they do not delay the main assembly stage.

Quality control

A system for checking the product at various stages of manufacture should be planned in order to control the quality of the finished product.

Modifications to the plan

It will help your final evaluation process if you keep a **diary** with records of how you changed your plans including details of how you coped when things went wrong. If the diary shows the progress you have made each day with the measurements and changes which occurred you will then be able to check back to find out what was done and what was omitted.

---

1 For one of your recent project designs produce a full manufacturing plan to include:
   a) working drawing
   b) cutting list
   c) planning schedule.

1.10 PRODUCT EVALUATION

BY THE END OF THIS SPREAD, YOU SHOULD BE ABLE TO:

■ test products that you have modelled or manufactured

■ evaluate products that you have made

Checking what you have done

Evaluation of your product is crucial to ensure the design work you have done achieves the criteria of the original brief and the specification you prepared. The evaluation will also analyse the success of the product using the views of the client or user.

Throughout your project you should be constantly evaluating your work. This can be done by annotating your design ideas, development work, costings and research. These judgements are known as **formative evaluations**; that is, they guide further design work and enable you as a designer to make decisions about the success of your designs as they develop. Record in your **diary** the details of problems that you have encountered during the project and explain how you have overcome them.

When you have finished manufacturing your product you will be expected to analyse it with a **final evaluation**. Begin the final evaluation of your product by positioning and using it where it will normally be used. Listed below are some questions that could be asked of your product:

☐ Does it fit in with the surroundings?
☐ Is it too large, too small?
☐ Is it easy to move or adjust?
☐ Is it durable?
☐ Does the user know how to use the product?
☐ Is it safe?

Formative evaluation

Spoke design for wheels – try different patterns for visual effect.

Will the long chain length require a guide?

Look at different handlebar shapes and positions for greater control.

Change visual effect of bicycle using different handlebar grips/tyres/saddle.

Specification list

• low recumbent riding position

• suit wide range of riders aged 15 – 30

• maximum visual effect

• small wheels to improve acceleration

• good handling characteristics

• single speed

• maximum comfort

Some items in your evaluation will be of a general nature and apply to most products. Some items will be unique to your particular product. Nothing must be overlooked.

Now look back at your specification and check the final product against it. For each aspect of your specification comment on how successful your design has been. Also evaluate how adequate the specification was.

User trials

Ask a likely user of your product for their views. Ask them to give honest and constructive criticism of your product. Get them to try it out in various circumstances. This is called a **field trial**.

A user trials the bicycle

Evaluation report

To finalise your evaluation, report on the following to sum up the success of your product:

☐ Was the design brief adequate?
☐ Was the specification adequate?
☐ Did the product cost any more than expected? What hidden costs were there?
☐ Could large quantities be made cheaply?
☐ Did the product work well?
☐ Is the product high quality and would it be useful for a long time?
☐ Are there areas for improvement or redesign?
☐ Outline your product's strengths and weaknesses.
☐ Did you plan the project effectively or did you run out of time?
☐ How would you approach the next Design and Technology project differently?
☐ Did you put enough effort into the project?
☐ Outline your personal strengths and weaknesses.

Evaluation Report

The Rider Recumbent bicycle has now been manufactured in concept form and it is time to evaluate its fitness-for-purpose against the original specification.

1 The low riding position is fun and has certainly turned a few heads out on the road. Rider control is not easy and different configurations of handlebar layout and wheelbase lengths will need to be trialled.

2 The bicycle is heavy but is well suited to city cruising. The bicycle could be lightened by using different wheels and saddle.

3 The bicycle cost was estimated at

---

1 Write a specification for a household kettle and then evaluate the kettle you have at home.

2 Choose a recent product that has been manufactured at school or college. Using the criteria outlined above evaluate the work, or work with a friend and evaluate each other's work.

2.1 SELECTION OF MATERIALS

BY THE END OF THIS SPREAD, YOU SHOULD BE ABLE TO:

- use the correct technical language to explain the qualities of different materials
- choose suitable materials for a particular job

Throughout the design of a product the material or materials from which it is to be made will be considered in great detail. It is extremely important to the success of the product to use the right material for every component part. Below is a **spider diagram** of some of the issues which may be discussed.

Choosing the right material

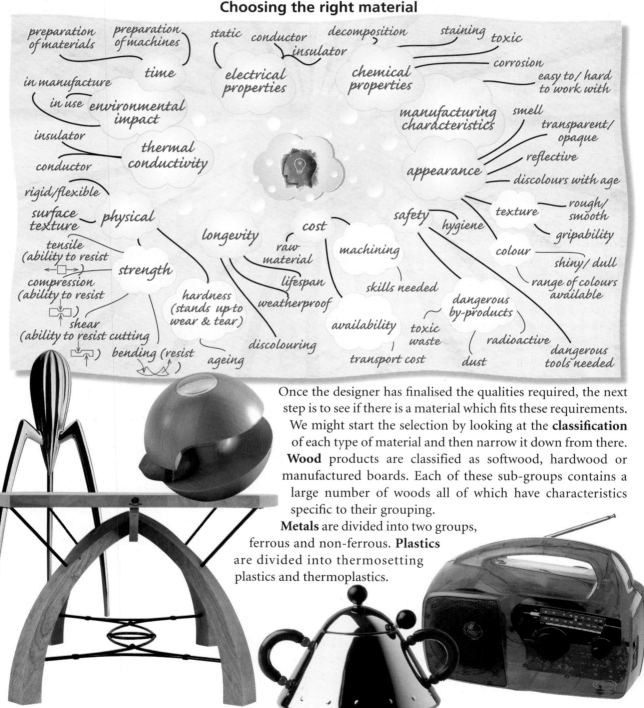

Once the designer has finalised the qualities required, the next step is to see if there is a material which fits these requirements. We might start the selection by looking at the **classification** of each type of material and then narrow it down from there. **Wood** products are classified as softwood, hardwood or manufactured boards. Each of these sub-groups contains a large number of woods all of which have characteristics specific to their grouping.

Metals are divided into two groups, ferrous and non-ferrous. **Plastics** are divided into thermosetting plastics and thermoplastics.

The table below takes a few of the qualities from the spider diagram opposite and demonstrates where you might expect to find most of the materials from a given group. There will, of course, be exceptions. Balsa wood, for example, is much lighter than other woods.

QUALITY MATCHING CHART

Qualities		WOOD			METAL		PLASTIC	
		Soft	Hard	Manufactured	Ferrous*	Non-ferrous	Thermoplastic	Thermosetting
Density	Heavy				✓			
	Average	✓	✓	✓		✓		
	Light					✓	✓	✓
Durability	V. resistant		✓		✓	✓	✓	✓
	Needs coating	✓	✓	✓	✓			
Waterproof	Water resistant				✓	✓	✓	✓
	Not water resistant	✓	✓	✓				
Colours	Wide range		✓	✓			✓	✓
	Restricted	✓	✓	✓	✓	✓		
Electrical properties	Conductor				✓	✓		
	Insulator	✓	✓	✓			✓	✓
	Static risk						✓	✓
Heat conductivity	Conductor				✓	✓	✓	
	Insulator	✓	✓	✓				✓
Cost	High		✓			✓		
	Low	✓		✓	✓		✓	✓
Workability	High skill input		✓		✓	✓		
	Care needed	✓	✓	✓	✓	✓	✓	✓
	Easy			✓				

* containing iron

1   How many categories of metal are there and what are they called? List the qualities you would look for in the material used to make a metal spoon.

2   A drinks company makes mugs and cups using clay. Unfortunately their supply of clay has become too expensive, so they need to find a new raw material. Suggest one and explain the reasons for your choice.

3   Think of a product which should be made using hardwood. Explain why the alternative materials are not so suitable.

2.2 MATERIALS TESTING FOR SUITABILITY

BY THE END OF THIS SPREAD, YOU SHOULD BE ABLE TO:

- understand how designers match their design ideas with materials
- understand some of the tests which might be used to test the suitability of any material

Key

material to be tested

In industry a whole project might be rejected unless the designer can show they have chosen the best materials to do the job. A great deal of money will be invested to test each material to see if it will cope adequately with its anticipated **environment**.

Comparing a range of materials

A dining room table top, for example, has to be strong enough to hold the weight of the dinner service, be resistant to the heat from the hot plates, resist scratching by the cutlery and above all look attractive for many years. The designer may find several materials which might be suitable. The next stage is to test these materials under scientifically controlled conditions.

Physical tests

The illustrations show some simple mechanical tests which could be used at school or college. More complex machines are used in industry which provide more reliable results.

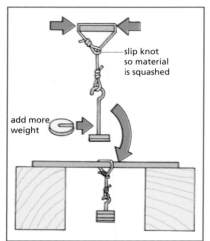

Test for bending

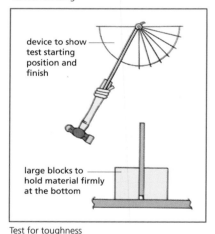

Test for toughness

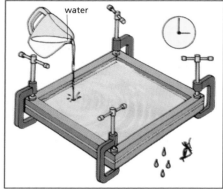

Time test to see how waterproof the material is

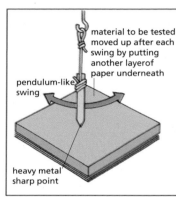

Test for hardness (scratchability)

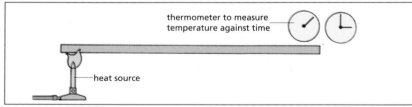

Test for heat conductivity

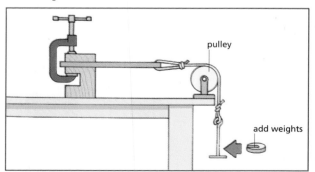

Test for tension

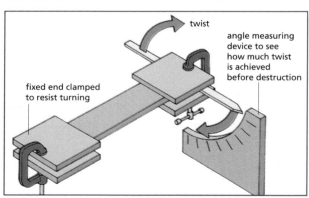

Test for resistance to torsion or twisting

28

Environmental tests

More specialised tests may have to be devised where the conditions in which the product is used might create problems. Things to consider include static electricity, vibration, dust, ultraviolet (UV) radiation, etc.

Prototyping

As the design progresses through the design process several models may be made. The models become more and more complex and soon begin to be almost indistinguishable from a final product. The next stage is to build a working model or **prototype**. The prototype uses the materials used in the real-life product rather than substituting other materials which are easier to handle. The prototype can be used to test other things besides the materials (see Spread 1.8). The prototype should be manufactured in a way closely resembling the process for the final product. In the case of the car, people can drive it to test for handling, visibility, comfort, etc.

Evaluation of assembled materials

The testing hasn't finished yet. The whole product can now be tested to see if the materials react well together. Where the products are used in potentially life-threatening situations they must be tested for **safety**. A car needs to pass rigorous tests set by both the manufacturer and the Ministry of Transport before it can go into full production.

Even after the product has been launched onto the market testing may still continue. Car magazines often commission safety tests from independent experts and then report the results. How a car handles in these tests can radically affect its sales.

The right choice of materials is therefore extremely important and may well decide whether a product is successful or not.

Safety test in a car

1 Why do we test materials for hardness?

2 Which tests would you do on the plastic which is intended to make a Frisbee?

3 All Saints Co. Ltd. have a massive factory in Scotland which makes glass models of pop stars. They can alter the brittleness of the glass by adding various chemicals, but these discolour the glass. Draw some illustrations to explain the tests they should do to see how many chemicals to add to their mixture so the models are not discoloured too much and can be sent safely around the world.

3.1 PREPARING WOOD FOR USE

BY THE END OF THIS SPREAD, YOU SHOULD BE ABLE TO:

- describe how wood is processed from felling to the wood yard
- identify damage when buying wood and be able to explain how this has occurred
- classify wood into its different types
- list the properties of each type of wood product

Wood has been a very popular **construction material** throughout history as it is a resource which is readily available, easy to use, versatile and renewable. Many woods can be worked as soon as they are cut down (called 'in the green') but this product will have a very high water content and may shrink, distort and split as it dries out. Consequently nearly all the wood we use today has its **moisture content** reduced from 40–60% of its weight to 10% during a process called **seasoning**.

Processing of wood

After **felling** (chopping down), the bark is removed and the tree is cut into planks. The wood from the centre of the trunk, called the 'heartwood', is the strongest. The 'sapwood' nearer the outside is weaker and has a higher moisture content. There are various ways in which the trunk can be divided up to maximise its commercial usefulness.

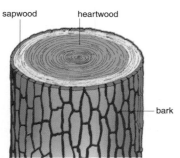

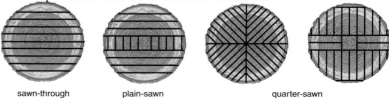

sawn-through   plain-sawn   quarter-sawn

Seasoning

The timber is dried in one of two ways: by stacking in open air drying racks or kiln drying in very large ovens. Kiln drying is much quicker but is expensive and can result in the wood warping or cracking. Air drying is less stressful for the wood but can only reduce moisture content to around 15% so kilns are used to finish the process. As the wood dries stresses are set up which can cause a variety of problems. Shrinkage movement is different depending upon where in the trunk the plank has been cut.

Storage

Wood is continually affected by the moisture content of its environment. Industries which carry large stocks of wood go to great expense to control the temperature and humidity so the wood is not damaged before use.

Classification of wood

Wood is classified into three types: softwood, hardwood and manufactured boards. **Softwoods** come from coniferous trees, which grow quickly with straight trunks and are often grown in plantations producing wood for construction and joinery. After the planks are cut the waste is made into manufactured boards and paper.

Hardwoods come from deciduous trees, which usually grow slowly with twisted trunks. They are being cut down quicker than they grow and consequently are becoming more and more expensive. However hardwoods are more durable and offer a wide range of colours and patterns, so they are highly prized by the specialist woodworker looking for these particular qualities.

Manufactured boards are becoming increasingly popular and are available in an ever-increasing range of sizes and finishes. They are made

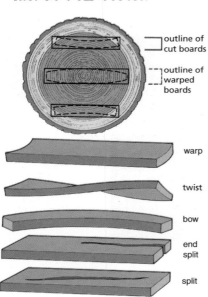

from the waste produced when the trunks and branches are cut into planks. The more expensive boards are made like a sandwich, having a good quality wood or veneer on the outside surfaces but a lower quality inside. The internal wood can be blocks, hence blockboard, or smaller chips (chipboard) or very small fibres, called medium-density fibreboard (MDF). Cheaper boards can be obtained without the external coating.

Plywood is made using several thin layers of wood with the grain running in alternate directions. Placing the grain like this overcomes the inherent weakness of wood and therefore makes plywood very strong for its weight and thickness compared with natural wood.

CHOOSING THE RIGHT WOOD OR BOARD

TYPE AND SIZES	CLASSIFICATION	WORKING CHARACTERISTICS	FINISH	COST
NATURAL WOODS – sold by the metre up to 5 m lengths:	**Softwoods:** Yellow cedar Deal, Pine	Easy to use due to straight grain and lack of knots	Good finish with pale colour	Low
Planks – sizes up to 300 × 50 mm;	Pirana pine	Easy to work Straight grain and lack of knots; less likely to chip	Light brown with red flashes – good quality	Low/Med
Strips – sizes below 100 mm but over 50 mm; *Squares* – up to 100 mm;	**Hardwoods:** Mahogany	Moderately difficult, need to go with the grain	Mid brown/red	Med/High
Dowels – diameters between 3 and 50 mm.	Oak	Moderately difficult	Pale brown colour, often open texture	Med/High
	Lime	Excellent for detailed work, soft to cut and close-grained	Very light yellow – very soft, colour darkens with exposure to light	Med
MANUFACTURED BOARDS – standard size – 1220 × 2440 mm	Veneered blockboard	Difficult, blocks leave poor edge and may need covering	Good if edges are matched	Med
Thicknesses – 3, 4, 6, 9, 12, 18, 22, 25 mm and occasionally greater	Plywood	Different outer veneers, very good otherwise Tendency to chip Blunts tools quickly	Depends upon grade of external face	Med/Low
	MDF	Easy – protect against dust Blunts tools quickly	Needs coating, usually paint	Low

1 (a) Which type of trees supply us with softwoods?
   (b) Why do we season wood before use?
   (c) What happens if the wood is seasoned too quickly?

2 A cabinet maker has been asked to make a high-quality table in a dark-coloured wood. Which wood should they choose and why?

3.2 CHOOSING AND MARKING OUT WOOD

BY THE END OF THIS SPREAD, YOU SHOULD BE ABLE TO:

- take a piece of wood and prepare it for use to a given size
- mark out wood using a range of tools

Choosing the wood

Ensure the wood is free from seasoning damage and knots. Knots can give the wood character but are more difficult to work and should be avoided near a joint.

Most wood is now sold in standard sizes with all the sides and edges smooth and clean. This is called planed all round (PAR). If the size you require is not standard then you may need to buy PSE – which means planed on one side and edge – and then prepare the other two to your requirements. Rough-sawn wood has no smooth sides or edges and you need to prepare it all yourself.

Marking face sides and edges and cutting to size

Because wood is a **hygroscopic** (affected by humidity/moisture), you may need to do some initial preparation to get the size exactly right. You need an even, smooth side and edge (see A below) to start with. These are called the face side and face edge. Use the flow chart below to get a piece of wood to size.

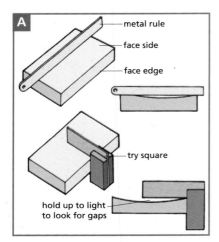

A
- metal rule
- face side
- face edge
- try square
- hold up to light to look for gaps

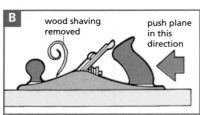

B
- wood shaving removed
- push plane in this direction

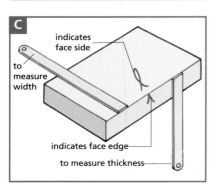

C
- indicates face side
- to measure width
- indicates face edge
- to measure thickness

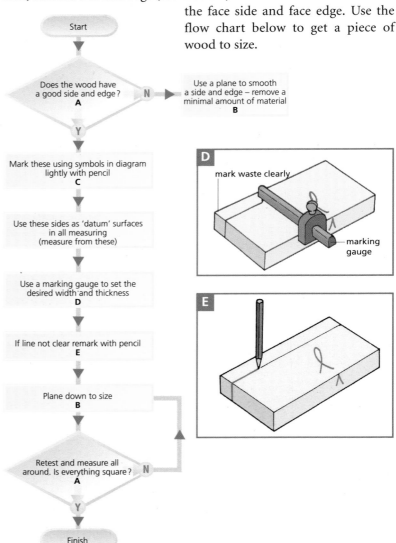

Start

Does the wood have a good side and edge?
A
— N → Use a plane to smooth a side and edge – remove a minimal amount of material
B

Y

Mark these using symbols in diagram lightly with pencil
C

Use these sides as 'datum' surfaces in all measuring (measure from these)

Use a marking gauge to set the desired width and thickness
D

If line not clear remark with pencil
E

Plane down to size
B

Retest and measure all around. Is everything square?
A
— N →

Y

Finish

D
- mark waste clearly
- marking gauge

E

Marking tools

Marking knife

Two pieces of wood are fixed together using joints (see pages 42 to 47). To get a very precise edge when cutting a joint many wood workers like to mark where they are going to cut using a marking knife. This accurately cuts through the surface fibres and ensures very sharp edges and a professional quality of finish. Notice the shape of the marking knife blade which has one flat edge so it can be placed exactly along the edge of the metal rule.

Dividers

Dividers have points at both ends and can be used to mark these shapes for cutting by trimming the fibres just like the marking knife.

waste to be removed   template made from thin metal

Bradawl

A bradawl has a sharp point which is pushed into wood to mark places for drilling or where screws are to be put in.

template angle:
1:6 - softwood
1:8 - hardwood

Using jigs and templates

If you have the same shape to mark out several times then you can use a template or jig. A template is any device which allows you to either mark out work accurately without measuring *or* go directly onto cutting out.

Template to mark out dovetail joints

The dovetail jig is used to speed up the manufacture of dovetail joints. The wood is clamped into this device and a router is used to cut the joint very accurately and with minimal preparation.

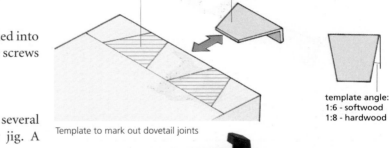

Dovetail jig

---

1 What does hygroscopic mean?

2 What is the difference between a piece of wood supplied PAR and one supplied PSE?

3 You have six friends to help you make 100 pieces of wood which have to measure $100 \times 50 \times 20$ mm. The raw material is supplied PSE (220 mm wide and 20 mm thick) in 4-metre lengths. How would you organise them to produce the pieces as efficiently as possible?

3.3 HAND TOOLS FOR CUTTING WOOD

BY THE END OF THIS SPREAD, YOU SHOULD BE ABLE TO:

- choose the right tool for a specific task
- understand the problems and difficulties associated with these tools

Tasks and skills using hand tools

Cutting wood using hand tools requires a great deal of practice and patience to achieve high quality results. Knowledge of both the wood and the vast range of tools available will help to achieve accurate cutting and finishing. Manufacturers constantly have to balance the advantages and disadvantages of machine and hand tools. This includes comparison of equipment costs for machine tools and labour costs for hand tools. The table below shows a selection of the most common hand tools for use in a wide range of tasks.

TYPE		TECHNICAL INFORMATION	TIPS
Saws large blade for cutting straight lines	Panel saw	Available with a variety of teeth. Set of teeth (roughness of blade) measured in TPI (teeth per inch); few teeth = rough cut	Wood must be supported well so that it does not move during cutting and split off when cut nears end
	Tenon saw		
	Dovetail saw		
Saws small blade for curves	Coping saw	Blade can turn to cut in any direction *and* cut can be away or towards handle	Use keyhole to support work being cut – teeth down in this case
Chisels for accurate cutting through wood	Firmer chisel	Blade 3–50 mm – general-purpose with/out mallet	Keep very sharp to minimise effort and accidents, and to maximise quality
	Bevel-edge chisel	Bevel helps get into tight corners for lightweight work without mallet; 3–50 mm blades	
	Mortise chisel	4–38 mm blades – heavy-duty mallet work	

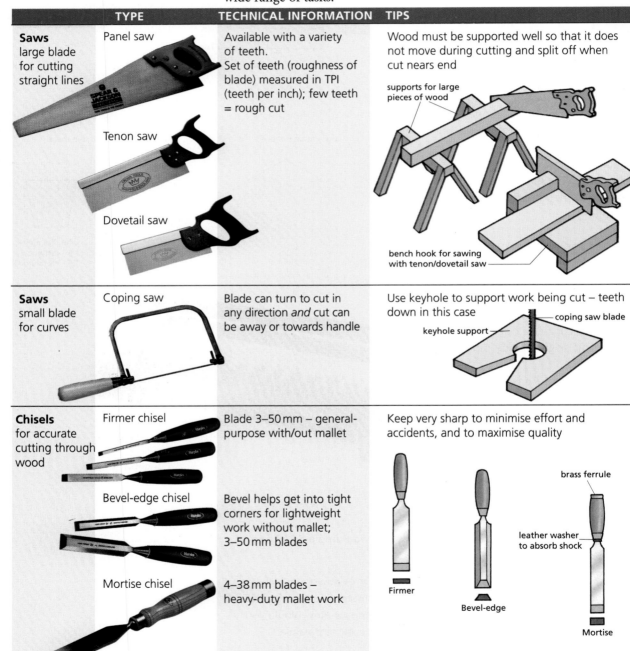

supports for large pieces of wood

bench hook for sawing with tenon/dovetail saw

coping saw blade

keyhole support

brass ferrule

leather washer to absorb shock

Firmer

Bevel-edge

Mortise

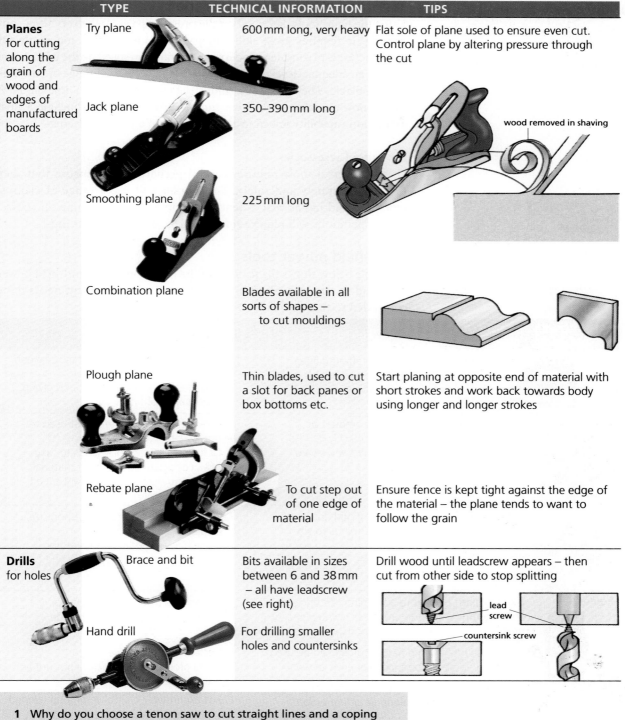

TYPE		TECHNICAL INFORMATION	TIPS
Planes for cutting along the grain of wood and edges of manufactured boards	Try plane	600 mm long, very heavy	Flat sole of plane used to ensure even cut. Control plane by altering pressure through the cut
	Jack plane	350–390 mm long	
	Smoothing plane	225 mm long	
	Combination plane	Blades available in all sorts of shapes – to cut mouldings	
	Plough plane	Thin blades, used to cut a slot for back panes or box bottoms etc.	Start planing at opposite end of material with short strokes and work back towards body using longer and longer strokes
	Rebate plane	To cut step out of one edge of material	Ensure fence is kept tight against the edge of the material – the plane tends to want to follow the grain
Drills for holes	Brace and bit	Bits available in sizes between 6 and 38 mm – all have leadscrew (see right)	Drill wood until leadscrew appears – then cut from other side to stop splitting
	Hand drill	For drilling smaller holes and countersinks	

wood removed in shaving

lead screw

countersink screw

1 Why do you choose a tenon saw to cut straight lines and a coping saw to cut curves?

2 Choose two examples of wood cutting which show the difference between a bevel-edge chisel and a mortise chisel.

3.4 POWER TOOLS FOR CUTTING WOOD

BY THE END OF THIS SPREAD, YOU SHOULD BE ABLE TO:

- identify common hand-held power tools and machine tools
- describe what these tools can do, and the possible disadvantages of using them

safety check:
Assess risk
Protective clothing
Eye protection
Extract fumes and dust
Guards in place

Tasks and skills using power tools

Using the hand tools described on the previous page can be very time-consuming. It requires great skill and patience and is often too costly for manufacturers to consider. Modern power tools can speed up the process and achieve an adequate level of quality. There is an increasing range of machine tools available. They may be for industrial use or for the DIY market. Each tool is now available in different motor sizes. These often include a **dust extraction** capability linked to a small bag or to a vacuum cleaner.

Power tool accessories

Using powerful tools requires careful preparation to ensure that they operate accurately and safely. The worker will use a range of clamps, templates and jigs as well as fences to help keep the machine on course. Some operations will require **safety guards** and **safety clothing**.

Hand-held power tools

The table below shows the features of the most common hand-held power tools and the traditional tools they replace. The **speed of cut** needs to be controlled so that the blades do not burn the wood surface.

HAND POWER TOOL	HAND TOOL REPLACED	FEATURES	DISADVANTAGES
Jigsaw	Coping saw	Cuts curved or straight lines through wood and boards up to medium thickness	1. Cuts on upstroke therefore face of wood spoilt 2. Blade tends to wobble and bend giving poor quality of finish ✱
Planer	Various planes	Removes large amount of manufactured quickly cutting all types of wood and board	1. Difficult to be accurate so not used to finish work 2. Quite hard to control – tends to take off inconsistent amounts of material unless you maintain a constant speed throughout cut ✱
Circular saw	Panel saws Tenon saws	Cuts hard/soft wood and manufactured boards to size	1. Restricted depth depending upon size of blade 2. Large blades need powerful motor
	Plough plane	Can cut grooves	
	Various planes	Can cut bevels	✱
Router	All moulding and plough planes	Used to do edging, slotting and joining processes giving a quality finish on all woods – especially MDF	1. Cannot cut less stable boards like chipboards due to speed of blade
	Vast range of tools	Combination cutters can be used to form joints at ends of wood	1. Cutters very expensive 2. Joints produced are practical but not as attractive as hand-sawn ones
		Used in conjunction with jig, cuts joints along length of wood	1. Jigs expensive – careful setting up needed ✱
Power sander Orbital sander	Sanding block	Various grades (coarseness) of paper available for a whole range of cutting down and finishing tasks	1. Care must be taken not to take away too much material 2. Using the right grade of paper is essential as coarse grade paper scratches wood badly ✱

✱ dust extraction needed

Machine power tools

Machine power tools are used in the home by DIY enthusiasts and progress in size and complexity up to massive machines used in industry. Some of the largest machines have multiple tool heads, which can do the same job at two or even four cutting points at the same time. These more complex machines may be semi-automatic or even computer controlled (see CAM, Spread 7.6).

As they all remove large amounts of material extremely quickly *they have serious health and safety risks* in both the operation of the machine and the production of waste. The wood is removed so quickly it needs a powerful extraction unit to take away dust and debris from the cutter to avoid clogging. The speed of cut is so fast that dust rather than shavings are produced. The dust is easily inhaled which can cause lung damage.

The table below shows the most common machine tools and the traditional tools they replace.

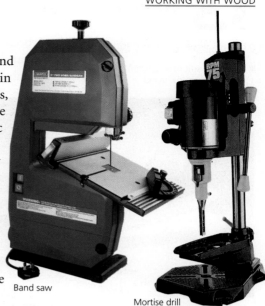

Band saw

Mortise drill

MACHINE TOOL	HAND TOOL REPLACED	FEATURES	DISADVANTAGES
Mortise cutter	Mortise chisel and mallet	Cuts square holes which can be joined to make joints	Can squash wood around hole so some preparatory work is required, especially in softer, more delicate woods
Planer (thicknesser)	Various planes	1. Can put two clean faces on wood from rough cut 2. Can adjust thickness to size 3. Can plane rebates	Wood pulled through machine using rollers: the distance between rollers dictates a minimum length of wood
Table saw	Panel saw	Used to rip down large pieces of wood and board to size	Power of the blade means great care needs to be taken
	Various planes	Used to cut concaves, rebates, mitres and for sizing wood. Health and safety rules dictate that concaves and rebates cannot be cut by students in schools.	
Radial arm saw	Panel saw Tenon saw	1. Cuts hard/soft wood across the grain 2. Rips down hard/soft wood to size 3. Cuts angles	1. Restricted to small pieces of wood and cannot cut sheets 2. Small depth of cut – no more than 100 mm 3. Must have kickback safety mechanism
Band saw	Panel saw Tenon saw Coping saw	1. Cuts across grain 2. Takes large sheets	1. Blade tends to bend/flex as it is thin and not supported 2. Restricted widths – blade inside side panel
Lathe	See woodturning lathe, Spread 3.5		

1 Which machine tool is used to cut square holes and which hand tool has it replaced?

2 Explain two health and safety risks associated with machine tools.

3 Explain how a router would have been used to make a product of your choice.

Planer (thicknesser)

3.5 SHAPING WOOD

BY THE END OF THIS SPREAD, YOU SHOULD BE ABLE TO:

- choose a suitable method to shape your chosen piece of wood

Wood is an extremely versatile material which can be shaped in many ways. It can be carved, cut or bent into a wide range of shapes, providing a suitable type and grade of wood is chosen.

Carving

Lime wood is usually recommended to be the best wood to carve. It is soft to cut and very close-grained so small details can be cut without them breaking off accidentally.

The shape is usually achieved by drawing the design on two faces of the block of timber. The waste is then removed from one side using a coping saw or band saw (see Spread 3.4) and taped back into place to support the second cut in the opposite plane. The design is then gradually cut away using chisels or **gouges**.

Turning using a lathe

One of the most exciting and satisfying methods of shaping wood is to use a lathe. This machine is used to spin the wood and provides a stable plinth on which to rest a cutting tool. The operator then carefully pushes the tool into the rotating wood and cuts away the waste. A vast range of patterns and designs can be made. The lathe can support wood in two ways. Firstly, long thin pieces can be held at both ends using either a **fork** (or occasionally a **chuck**) at the **drive centre** end, and a pointed spike at the other end (the **tailstock centre**). Legs for tables and chairs are made this way. A router can also be used with a lathe to cut complex patterns like barleytwist, etc.

Larger, flatter pieces of wood can be turned using a device called a **faceplate**. The wood is first temporarily glued to a sacrificial piece of waste material using a glue and paper sandwich. The sacrificial piece is then screwed to the faceplate ensuring the workpiece has no screw holes in it at all. The paper sandwich ensures that the workpiece can be separated easily from the sacrificial wood at the end of the job. Fruit bowls are just one example of the many things which can be made in this way using a whole variety of woods. A favourite with many woodworkers is walnut burr because of its incredible grain patterns.

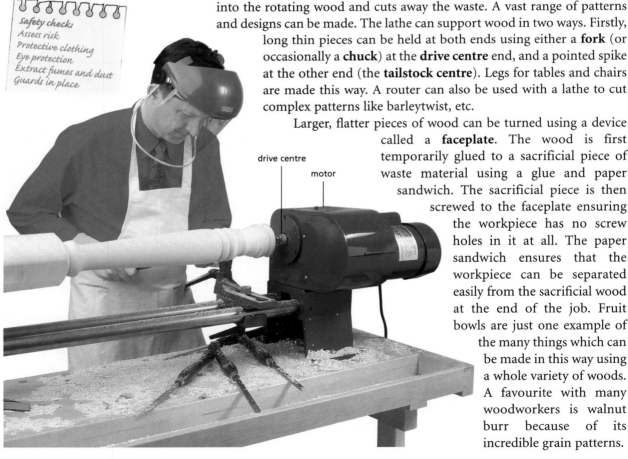

safety check:
Assess risk
Protective clothing
Eye protection
Extract fumes and dust
Guards in place

drive centre

motor

Using a plane

A plane can be used to cut a flat surface on any of the faces of a piece of wood. Planes come in a variety of sizes. As a general rule you should use the largest one you can comfortably handle which fits onto the piece of wood. This gives you the largest **sole** of the plane in contact with the wood and therefore a much greater chance of planing a flat surface. To achieve a good quality of cut the blade needs to be adjusted for straightness and depth of cut. The wood needs to be cut in the right direction, *not* against the grain. Cutting across the end grain requires a sharp blade, a **shooting board** (to support the wood) and a small depth of cut (see diagram below).

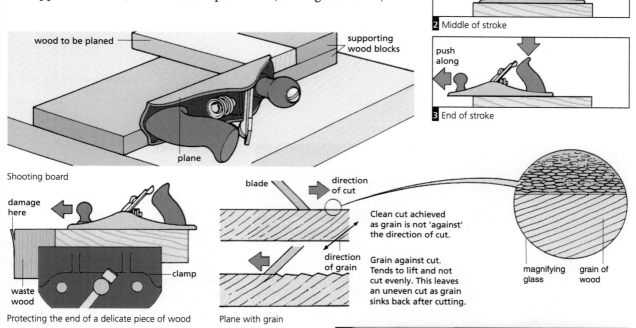

PLANING TECHNIQUE

1 Start of planing stroke — push down, push along

2 Middle of stroke — push down

3 End of stroke — push along

wood to be planed

supporting wood blocks

plane

Shooting board

damage here

clamp

waste wood

Protecting the end of a delicate piece of wood

blade — direction of cut

Clean cut achieved as grain is not 'against' the direction of cut.

direction of grain

Grain against cut. Tends to lift and not cut evenly. This leaves an uneven cut as grain sinks back after cutting.

magnifying glass   grain of wood

Plane with grain

Specialist planes

There are also specialist planes which do not cut across the whole surface of the wood. A **rebate plane** will cut a channel from the edge of the wood. A **plough plane** cuts out a groove which is often used to insert the base of a box or thin back to shelves etc. The edge of a piece of wood can also be decorated using a **moulding plane**.

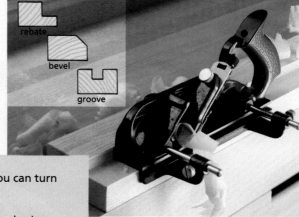

rebate

bevel

groove

Specialist rebate plane

1 Find out how you decide the maximum size of wood you can turn between centres on a wood lathe.

2 What is the sacrificial wood used for when turning a bowl using a faceplate?

3 Look carefully at the planing technique. What would happen to the wood if you pressed down where 'push along' is written?

3.6 FORMING WOOD

BY THE END OF THIS SPREAD, YOU SHOULD BE ABLE TO:

- bend wood using a variety of techniques
- identify wood that has been formed – and the technique that has been used

Forming is another word for bending wood into curves for use in furniture frames, for example. Some woods bend much more easily than others, particularly when unseasoned (green), but when you release the pressure they will return to their original shape.

It is possible to bend quite thick pieces of wood around shallow curves using a series of cuts called **kerfs**. These are cut across the grain and are then used to form the inside of the curve. However, the spacing of these cuts and the depth have to be very carefully calculated to achieve an accurate curve and the outside wood often splits.

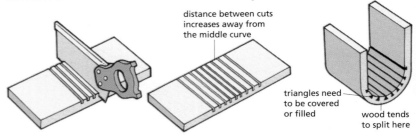

distance between cuts increases away from the middle curve

triangles need to be covered or filled

wood tends to split here

Cutting kerfs using a tenon saw

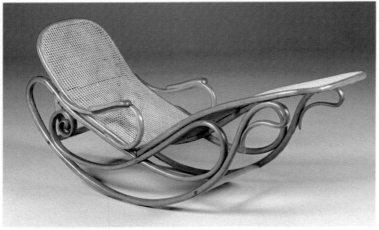

A steam-bent rocking chair

A laminated plywood chair

Steam bending

If the wood will not bend without snapping it can be made more supple by increasing its **moisture content**. This can be achieved by soaking or, for more flexibility still, held in steam. A length of timber which has been steamed will become incredibly flexible. Once moulded to the shape required it is held in this position using a **former** (a mould) and series of clamps until it cools and loses its moisture content. Even when dry the timber will not usually hold its shape without some sort of support.

Laminated shapes

A more successful way to achieve quite tight bends without the risk of splitting is to use **laminated plywood**. A 4 mm thick piece of ply behaves like it has a grain because it only has one thickness of ply in the middle. It will bend more easily in one direction than another. If this flexibility is not enough then further bending can be achieved by wetting it or steaming. Several strips of ply are then placed into a former. This needs to be very strong as the ply will exert great pressure to resist the bending. The former is usually lined with cork to avoid damaging the outside surface of the plywood. A thin layer of glue between each plywood layer is needed (usually PVA – see page 48). A layer of plastic is used to stop excess glue sticking the shape to the former. Finally the clamps are tightened, starting from the inside of the curve. This allows each sheet of the plywood to slip gently across the surface of the next as the shape is made. Great care needs to be taken to ensure there are no gaps between each layer as this would weaken the structure considerably.

If **wood veneers** are used they need to be selected very carefully as many will split. It is much more likely that wetting or steaming will be needed to achieve the amount of bending required. More clamping blocks will also be needed. An advantage, though, is that different coloured woods can be used. This can add interest and texture to the final piece which is not attainable in any other way. The veneers more prone to splitting can be put in the middle of the sandwich.

Veneers have been used to make this violin look attractive.

BENDING WOOD VENEERS

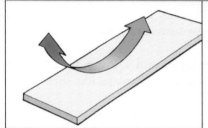

1 Check this is direction of easiest bending.

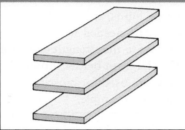

2 Cut required number (minimum 3). Cut too long.

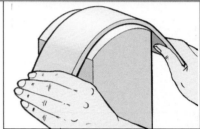

3 Test to establish if wetting or steaming will be needed.

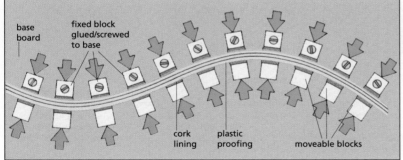

base board · fixed block glued/screwed to base · cork lining · plastic proofing · moveable blocks

4 Make the mould – cut the blocks and space them so that flat edges allow clamping – fix blocks firmly to bottom board.

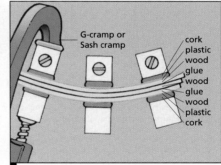

G-cramp or Sash cramp · cork · plastic · wood · glue · wood · glue · wood · plastic · cork

5 Tighten G-cramp around blocks.

---

1 Find something which has been made, or could have been made, by bending wood. Explain which technique is probably used to manufacture it.

2 What are the disadvantages of using kerfs to bend a piece of wood?

3 When laminating plywood what mistake must be avoided to ensure the shape is structurally sound?

3.7 JOINING WOOD: CARCASES

- name the three categories of joints
- use your knowledge of carcase joints to choose the most appropriate for a given job

Joints fit into three categories depending upon the shape which is being made. They are either **carcase** (hollow shape with flat sides like a box or wardrobe, etc.), **framework,** or **edge-to-edge** joints.

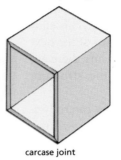

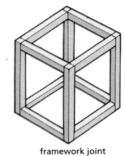

carcase joint   framework joint   edge-to edge

Making a carcase

Joining wood can be done by simply gluing the two surfaces together. This is called a **butt joint** and is extremely weak, especially when the gluing area is small or the end grain is used. Woodworkers over the years have developed a vast range of joints to suit all situations. Generally the more complex joints are the strongest. However, more time and skill will probably be needed to make them. An increased gluing area will also contribute to the strength of a joint.

The diagram below shows corner joints and T-joints for carcases. T-joints are used for cross members within the carcase, like shelves and dividers, for example.

CORNER JOINTS FOR CARCASES

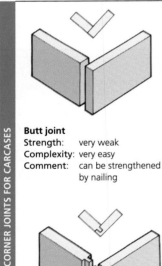

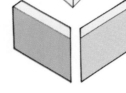

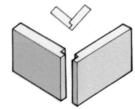

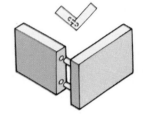

Butt joint
Strength: very weak
Complexity: very easy
Comment: can be strengthened by nailing

Mitre joint
Strength: very weak
Complexity: difficult without mitred shooting block or sander
Comment: can be strengthened with dowels and tongues

Lap or rebate joint
Strength: average
Complexity: easy
Comment: can be made more interesting by a longer interlock

Dowel joint
Strength: average strength
Complexity: easy – especially using jig to line up holes accurately
Comment: can be butt or mitred

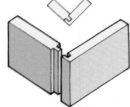

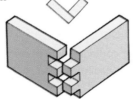

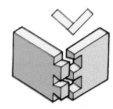

Groove and rebate joint
Strength: average strength
Complexity: surprisingly difficult
Comment: only used on thicker wood so that pin does not break

Finger joint
Strength: strong
Complexity: difficult
Comment: looks very effective

Dovetail joint
Strength: extra strong
Complexity: very difficult
Comment: looks very effective. Need different cut angles for hard and softwoods

T-JOINTS FOR CARCASES

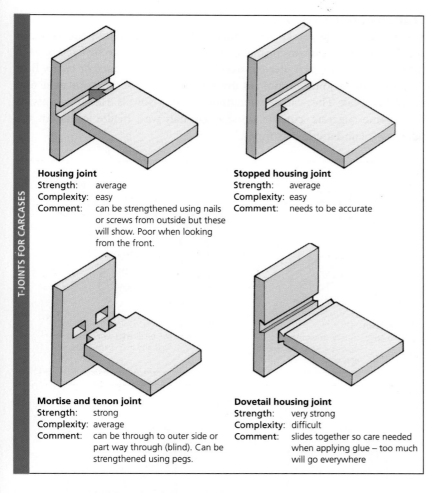

Housing joint
Strength: average
Complexity: easy
Comment: can be strengthened using nails
                  or screws from outside but these
                  will show. Poor when looking
                  from the front.

Stopped housing joint
Strength: average
Complexity: easy
Comment: needs to be accurate

Mortise and tenon joint
Strength: strong
Complexity: average
Comment: can be through to outer side or
                  part way through (blind). Can be
                  strengthened using pegs.

Dovetail housing joint
Strength: very strong
Complexity: difficult
Comment: slides together so care needed
                  when applying glue – too much
                  will go everywhere

Joining manufactured boards

A more limited range of joints can be used on manufactured boards. Many of the boards do not have the internal strength found in natural wood. This means the delicate shaping involved in cutting dovetails is often impossible. Plywood is strong enough to hold finger joints but most of the other boards are best joined with dowel joints or physical fittings like knock-down joints (see Spread 3.10). A veneered board needs a joint which does not expose the inferior wood at the ends and therefore a mitred joint of some sort is essential.

1 What is the difference between a carcase and a framework?

2 Compare a butt joint with a dovetail joint listing as many differences as possible.

3 Draw a freehand sketch of a large chest which has been built using a carcase method. Label all the joints you would use to build it and explain why you have chosen those particular joints.

3.8 JOINING WOOD: FRAMEWORK

- use your knowledge of joints to select the most appropriate ones for building a framework

Framework corners

The joints in frameworks are similar to those used to join carcases (see previous spread). However, smaller areas of wood have to be fixed to each other. The ends of each piece of wood can only be cut once or twice. Butt joints and mitre joints do not cut through the width of the wood at all and are rather weak. They can be strengthened using dowels. Halving joints, as their name suggests, cut the wood once, half way. Bridle joints cut the wood twice and are the strongest.

Preparing a mitre joint on a picture frame

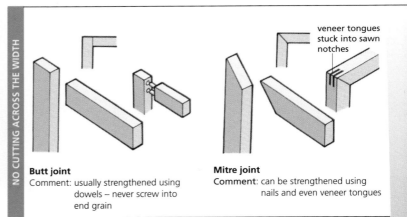

NO CUTTING ACROSS THE WIDTH

Butt joint
Comment: usually strengthened using dowels – never screw into end grain

veneer tongues stuck into sawn notches

Mitre joint
Comment: can be strengthened using nails and even veneer tongues

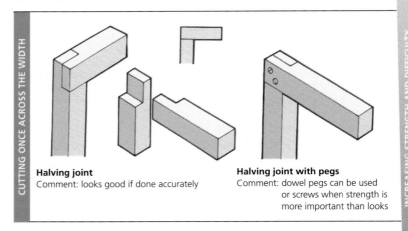

CUTTING ONCE ACROSS THE WIDTH

Halving joint
Comment: looks good if done accurately

Halving joint with pegs
Comment: dowel pegs can be used or screws when strength is more important than looks

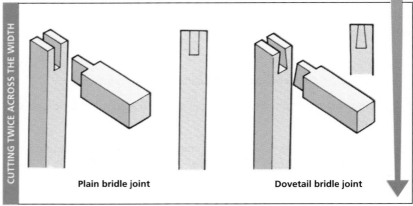

CUTTING TWICE ACROSS THE WIDTH

Plain bridle joint

Dovetail bridle joint

INCREASING STRENGTH AND DIFFICULTY

Mortise and tenon joints

These are a real favourite with woodworkers everywhere. They are the most satisfying to make and offer great strength as they combine an interlocking system with a large gluing area. Different types of joint are shown below. Notice how the names correspond to the tools which make each part. A tenon saw is used to cut the tenon and a mortise chisel is used to cut the mortise.

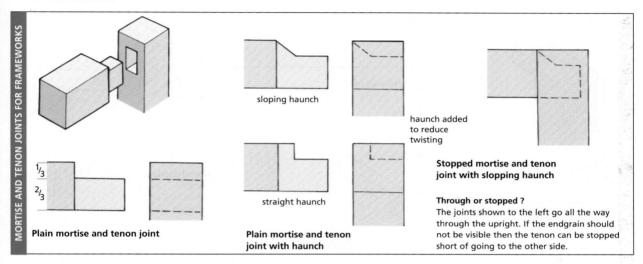

MORTISE AND TENON JOINTS FOR FRAMEWORKS

$\frac{1}{3}$

$\frac{2}{3}$

Plain mortise and tenon joint

sloping haunch

straight haunch

Plain mortise and tenon joint with haunch

haunch added to reduce twisting

Stopped mortise and tenon joint with slopping haunch

Through or stopped ?
The joints shown to the left go all the way through the upright. If the endgrain should not be visible then the tenon can be stopped short of going to the other side.

T-joints in a framework

As a framework is made from thinner strips of wood it is lighter than most carcases of the same size. To achieve this a certain amount of strength is lost. Adding cross members can improve the strength without adding too much weight. A whole range of T-joints have evolved to do this.

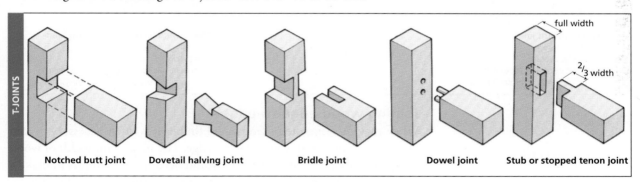

T-JOINTS

full width

$\frac{2}{3}$ width

Notched butt joint   **Dovetail halving joint**   **Bridle joint**   **Dowel joint**   **Stub or stopped tenon joint**

1 Which part of a joint is called the mortise?

2 Smart Art UK Ltd. are a company printing a wide range of posters which need to be fitted into a simple frame. As chief designer which joint would you recommend for the frame and why?

3 Draw a framework which could be used to support three shelves. Show the joints in detail and explain why you chose them.

Three-way joints

Occasionally designers are faced with problems which cannot be overcome using the standard joints on the previous two spreads. For example, at the top of table or chair legs a three-way joint is required. The diagram below shows a range of possible alternatives. The same balance between time and skill against strength and complexity still needs to be decided.

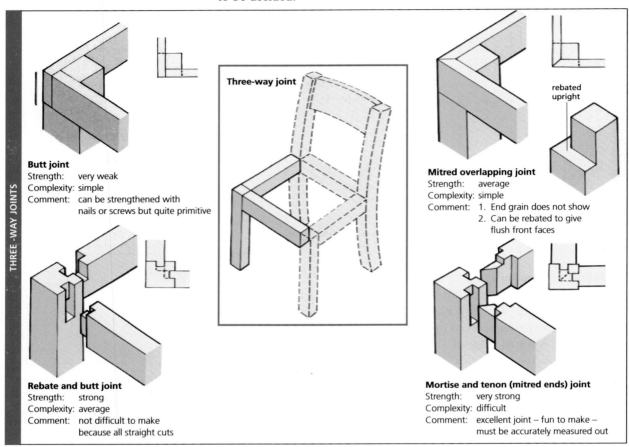

THREE-WAY JOINTS

Three-way joint

Butt joint
Strength: very weak
Complexity: simple
Comment: can be strengthened with
            nails or screws but quite primitive

Rebate and butt joint
Strength: strong
Complexity: average
Comment: not difficult to make
            because all straight cuts

rebated upright

Mitred overlapping joint
Strength: average
Complexity: simple
Comment: 1. End grain does not show
            2. Can be rebated to give
               flush front faces

Mortise and tenon (mitred ends) joint
Strength: very strong
Complexity: difficult
Comment: excellent joint – fun to make –
            must be accurately measured out

Joining wood edge-to-edge

When making larger items from solid timber it is often necessary to join one or more pieces of wood edge-to-edge. The maximum width of wood available is about 300 mm and you would need more than this to make a table top, for example. Designers often choose small widths and join them together to achieve the width they require. By combining small widths carefully it is possible to avoid distortion due to shrinkage. This can occur along annual rings as the wood's moisture levels alter due to changes in its environment (see Spread 3.1).

When making a table top, for example, the wood is laid out so that the grain 'cups' alternately up and then down (see left). Careful preparation is needed so that the edges match perfectly and the grain patterns look attractive.

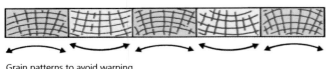

Grain patterns to avoid warping

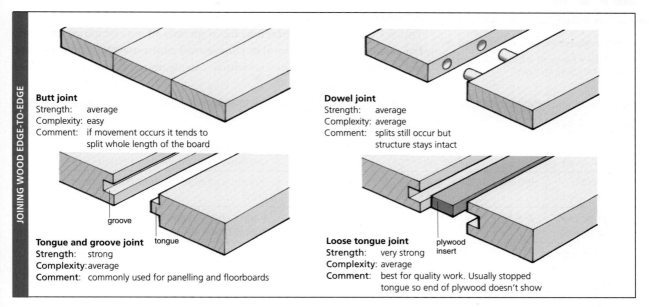

JOINING WOOD EDGE-TO-EDGE

Butt joint
Strength: average
Complexity: easy
Comment: if movement occurs it tends to
              split whole length of the board

Dowel joint
Strength: average
Complexity: average
Comment: splits still occur but
              structure stays intact

groove

Tongue and groove joint   tongue
Strength: strong
Complexity: average
Comment: commonly used for panelling and floorboards

Loose tongue joint   plywood
Strength: very strong   insert
Complexity: average
Comment: best for quality work. Usually stopped
              tongue so end of plywood doesn't show

Fitting panels

Panels are often used at the back of wardrobes or other free-standing pieces of furniture. The method of fabrication begins with the construction of a framework. A groove is then run along the inside of each side into which a thin plywood sheet is usually fitted. Inserting a panel is also the most common method of fitting a base into a box or small container.

A similar method is also used to support dividers within a carcase. Plywood and simple halving joints give support to the internal structure.

Grooves are also used as a jointing method when inserting solid wood as decorative panels.

FITTING PANELS BACKS AND BOTTOMS

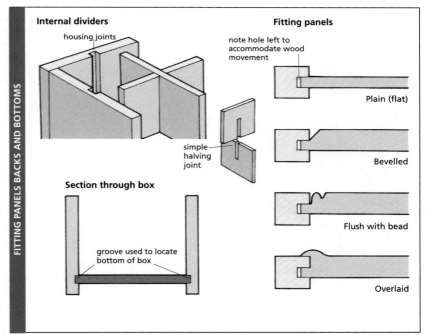

Internal dividers
housing joints
simple halving joint

Section through box
groove used to locate bottom of box

Fitting panels
note hole left to accommodate wood movement
Plain (flat)
Bevelled
Flush with bead
Overlaid

---

1   Draw the end grain of a table top made from joining planks edge to edge. Explain why it is done this way.

2   Which is the strongest three-way joint and why?

3   Use this page and the previous two spreads to design a money box. Draw out the design indicating clearly the joints which you have used and the woods which you have chosen.

By the end of this spread, you should be able to:

- choose glues to use in certain situations
- describe a range of mechanical fixings and when they are used

Adhesives

The wood joints on the previous three spreads all require gluing together. For convenience most school or college workshops use PVA, but this is not necessarily the only adhesive which can be used. Below is a table of adhesive properties.

NAME	WORKING TIME	APPLICATION	WATER-PROOF	GAP FILLING	COMMENTS
Scotch glue (animal glue)	6 hrs*	Warmed in water jacket glue pot	✗	✗	Comes in 'pearls' which need soaking first: excellent glue but hard to prepare/apply
Glue sticks	Instant	Glue gun	✓	✓	Stringing of glue commonplace – poor quality finish
Synthetic resin (ready mixed)	2–4 hrs*	Brushed on	✓	✓	Trade name 'Cascamite', excellent glue where joint is under stress
Synthetic resin (resin/hardener separate)	1–2 hrs*	Brushed on	✓	✓	For example 'Aerolite 300' or '306' – hardener applied to one surface, resin to the other
PVA (polyvinyl acetate)	1 hr	Brushed on	✗	✗	Easy to use – little initial bond therefore clamping essential. Waterproof type available
Contact adhesive	Instant	Plastic applicator	✓	✓	For example 'Evostik' – apply glue to both surfaces – works on contact, occasionally used when veneering
'Super glues'	Instant	Direct from nozzle	✗	✓	Very strong; hazardous in use; very costly – good for very small joints and delicate work where clamping is impossible

* All but instant glues need overnight clamping to harden.

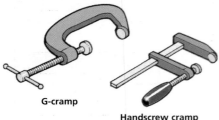

G-cramp

Handscrew cramp
Adjustable angle of grip

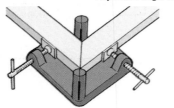

Mitre clamps

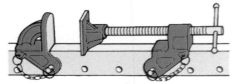

Sash cramp
For very large pieces

Applying glue

When applying glue to a wood joint great care must be taken not to get the glue on any surface which does not need it. As wood is porous glue will quickly seep into the grain and be very difficult to remove. It might not really show until the final finish is applied, but being water-resistant it will not absorb finishes like the wood surrounding it. The resulting mark will be almost impossible to remove.

Since many glues take some time to set it is usual to clamp the pieces together using a range of clamping devices how small blocks of waste wood have protect the wood from the metal of the faces. These are called clamping blocks.

Bench holdfast

Mechanical fixings

Joining wood with screws

Accurately sized holes must be drilled in preparation for inserting screws. This ensures the top piece of wood is pulled down firmly onto the lower piece. Used in conjunction with glue this is a very effective method of joining although screw heads may need disguising.

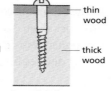

Countersunk screw
– for joining thick pieces of wood

Roundhead screw
– for joining pieces of wood of various thickness

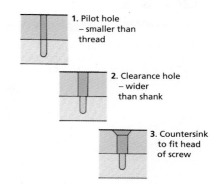

1. Pilot hole
   – smaller than thread

2. Clearance hole
   – wider than shank

3. Countersink to fit head of screw

Types of screw hole

Joining wood with nails

Nailing is not as strong as using screws. The nails work by pressing outwards onto the wood which means they always have the potential to split it down the grain. Oval nails are designed to prevent this. Nail heads will usually need to be covered.

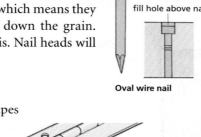

place oval wire nail along grain lines

fill hole above nail

Oval wire nail

Panel pin
– tiny nail used for delicate work
– head covered as for oval nail

Round wire nail
– more rustic work
– head usually remains showing

Joining wood with hinges

Hinges come in a vast range of shapes and sizes, each designed to do a specific job. They all rely on screw fixings so pilot holes and a good depth of material below the hinge are essential. Accurate fitting is needed if the hinge is to work smoothly.

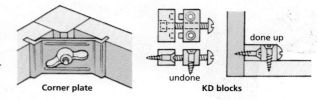

Piano hinge
very long – cut to fit length required

Butt hinge
recessed into work

Cylinder hinge
allows 180° movement

Concealed cabinet hinge
for manufactured boards

Joining with knock-down (KD) fittings

Used primarily with cheaper furniture made from manufactured boards like chipboard. This allows the item to be assembled quickly and with the minimum of skill once it has travelled home in 'flat pack' form.

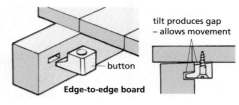

Corner plate

done up

undone

KD blocks

Joining boards to frames

Manufactured boards just need a screw attachment. However, wood boards made by edge-to-edge joining need joints which allow the natural movement of the wood. They are fixed into the stretchers using L-blocks so that movement is accommodated.

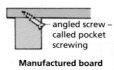

tilt produces gap
– allows movement

button

Edge-to-edge board

1 What are knock-down fittings and how do they work?

2 Why do we use clamping blocks?

3 What would be the best glue to use if you were mass-producing wooden chairs? Which would be your second choice of glue? Explain why you have chosen the first in preference to the second.

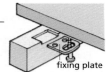

angled screw –
called pocket screwing

Manufactured board

fixing plate

3.11 WOOD MANUFACTURING IN QUANTITY

BY THE END OF THIS SPREAD, YOU SHOULD BE ABLE TO:

- understand the various tools and techniques used to achieve the speed and the accuracy required when manufacturing in quantity

In the school or college workshop we are often designing and making one protype. Even so, this may require the manufacture of many similar components or joints. Consequently designers have devised many time-saving devices for processes which have to be repeated many times.

Templates and jigs

Possibly the simplest of these is a metal template which is used to mark out dovetail joints very quickly. It simply hooks over the end of a piece of wood and ensures that the slant on the dovetail is identical on both pins and tails.

The **dovetail template** has been superseded in many places by the **router**. The router is like a drill which can cut sideways as well as into the wood. One of the many sets of cutters available is used to cut dovetails. To ensure the accuracy of the position of each tail and pin a **jig** is used to guide the cutter into the right place. To speed things up further both parts of the joint are cut simultaneously.

Some of the other tools available which can be used to cut other joints or produce **mouldings** very quickly are shown here. (A moulding is a decorative shape cut into the side or edge of a piece of wood. It might be used for a picture frame, for example.)

Metal template ...   is moved along ...   to give identical joints.

Marking out dovetails using a template

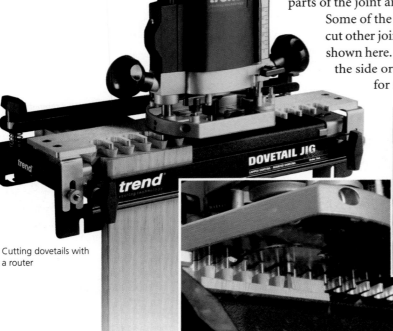

Cutting dovetails with a router

Cutting a moulding with a router

safety check:
Assess risk
Protective clothing
Eye protection
Extract fumes and dust
Guards in place

In industry

The router and jig method of manufacture is not used when a very large number of components are to be made. Setting up a jig and machinery takes too long and requires some skill. Mass manufacture requires the wood to be positioned accurately, clamped firmly, cut to shape and expelled in a way that allows the process to be repeated over and over again at speed. This could be achieved manually using a relatively unskilled operator or automatically using computer-controlled machinery. (See CAM, Spread 7.6.)

Parker Knoll make chair legs using a machine which has several routers working automatically to cut the wood to shape. You can see a simplified diagram of the machining process below. The operator places the wood in the clamps and closes the safety guard. The wood moves clockwise and the first cut is made with the router moving along one face of the material. Cuts 2 and 3 are also being done on previously loaded wood. Simultaneously the operator is unloading a new chair leg and positioning the next piece of timber.

Four chair panels being cut simultaneously using a computer-controlled router

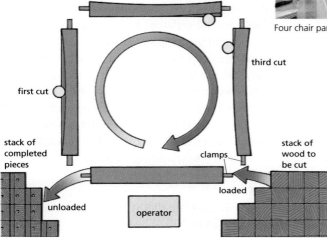

If the wood has to be shaped along its length then another version of the router will be used. When the router is fixed under a cutting table and the work passes over it the machine is called a **spindle moulder**. For complex mouldings, like banister rails, the cutters are placed in two opposing pairs. The wood can now be continuously fed through the machine and is cut into the desired shape.

continuous feed

Two pairs of router cutters used to mould a banister rail

1 What is a dovetail template and why is it used?

2 Someone working in her own home workshop might be cutting the same dovetail joint as the chair manufacturers down the road. What are the major differences in the way that these two work?

3 How could you decide if a piece of furniture was mass-manufactured or individually made? Which would be the most expensive to buy and why?

3.12 FINISHING WOODWORK

BY THE END OF THIS SPREAD, YOU SHOULD BE ABLE TO:

- describe what is meant by a 'finish' and why one is required
- choose an appropriate finish for a given situation

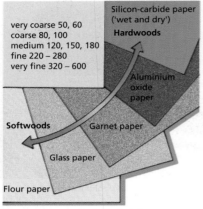

Abrasive paper grades (collectively known as sandpaper)

Silicon-carbide paper ('wet and dry')

Hardwoods

very coarse 50, 60
coarse 80, 100
medium 120, 150, 180
fine 220 – 280
very fine 320 – 600

Aluminium oxide paper

Softwoods

Garnet paper

Glass paper

Flour paper

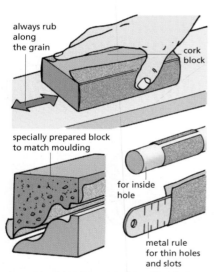

always rub along the grain

cork block

specially prepared block to match moulding

for inside hole

metal rule for thin holes and slots

Once the major manufacturing work has been completed all woods need to be 'finished'. This is a coating which will protect the wood from moisture, heat, knocks, dust and dirt, and also improve its appearance. Various methods can be used to achieve this. The one chosen will depend upon factors such as the environment the wood is to be used in, the type of wood, and the quality of the wood used.

Hardwoods, for example, are durable and usually beautiful to look at, and need little more than additional colour to enhance the grain patterns, and a good shine. **Softwoods** need colour and waterproofing, especially if they are to be used outdoors. At the other extreme, **manufactured boards** (without veneers) are covered over completely as their external coats are unsightly without attention to finish.

Preparation

A good quality finish can only be achieved if the surface below is completely flat. This is achieved by rubbing down with an **abrasive paper**, usually wrapped around a cork block. Several different grades of paper might be used, starting with a rough one, and working steadily down to fine grades until the surface feels very smooth. A typical choice for softwood might be first 100, then 180 and finally 280 grade. At this stage it is very important to apply the finish quickly as the wood is particularly susceptible to staining from moisture, dirt and natural oil from your hands. Fine papers may be needed again between coats, especially if the finish is water-based. This is called **cutting back**. The quality of the finish often depends upon the number of coats and the care taken whilst cutting back.

Application of finishes

There are so many types of finish available that it is difficult to work out exactly which to choose. The flow chart below should help.

Projects made in schools or colleges use a range of finishes applied by either brush or cloth. This is cost-effective because of the wide range of projects manufactured, all needing different finishes. However, the process is slow because of the need for several coats with cutting back if a professional quality is to be achieved.

In industry, sprayed finishes are becoming more common as they are automated and faster. However, they are expensive to set up due to the cost of the spray machinery and safety precautions. Spraying needs little or no

WHICH FINISH ?												
Type of wood	Hardwood				Softwood				Man-made boards			
Environment	Internal		External		Internal		External		Internal		External	
Additional colour?	Colour	Clear	Colour	Clear	Colour	Clear	Colour	Clear	Colour	Clear	Colour	Clear
Finish (see table opposite)	1 with 8 2 with 8 2 with 9 5, 4, 7	1 2 4 5	2 with 8 2 with 9 6, 7	2 5	2 with 3 2 with 8 4, 7	2 4	7 2 with 3 2 with 8	2	2 with 3 7 2 with 8 2 with 9	2	6 2 with 9	2

cutting back because the spray is so fine and goes on more evenly. Drying time can be speeded up using ovens and a conveyor system if necessary. Little paint is wasted as the extraction system (for health and safety) is designed to pull the paint, and its fumes, away from the operator onto the job. Toxic fumes are then filtered before being expelled into the atmosphere.

FINISH	APPLICATION	USES	NOTES
1 French polish	Small cloth-covered pad	High quality furniture	1. May be preceded by colouring 2. Requires high level of skill to apply
2 Polyurethane varnish	Brush or spray	Furniture and wood fittings	1. Used as final waterproofing surface 2. Could be used on natural wood or coloured dye or paint
3 Water-based paint	Brush or cloth	Smaller wood artefacts like toys etc.	1. Used as opaque colour or watered down to show grain 2. Raises the grain 3. Needs top coat to proof
4 Wax polish	Cloth or spray	Furniture and anything wooden	1. Based on beeswax 2. Range of colours available 3. Good for achieving a good shine quickly – but short-lived!
5 Oil	Brush or cloth	Furniture, particularly made of teak	1. Teak oil – for teak (also called Danish) 2. Linseed oil – for cricket bats 3. Salad bowl oil – for woods used to hold food
6 Preservative e.g. creosote	Brush, spray or dipped	Exterior wood e.g. fences, sheds	1. Some very toxic 2. Needs care and protective clothing
7 Oil-based paint	Brush or spray	Interior and exterior joinery and fittings	1. Vast range of colours 2. Available in drip/non-drip – gloss/matt 3. Skill needed to achieve gloss finish
8 Water-based dye	Cloth or fine brush	All types of wood products	1. Precedes final proofing coat 2. Susceptible to damage between coats 3. Raises grain – so cutting back needed
9 Spirit-based dye	Brush or cloth	All types of wood products	1. Precedes final proofing coat 2. Cannot be used before water-based varnishes or French polish

Adapted from Construction Materials, John Cave, Nelson/Blackie, ISBN 0–17–438535–8

1 What is meant by the term 'cutting back'?

2 Which finish would you use to complete a hardwood garden chair, and why?

3 You are the person in charge of the Finish Department at Derriere Chair Co. Ltd. List the advantages your company would gain if they changed from using brushes to using a new spray system.

4.1 CHOOSING AND PREPARING METALS

- prepare metals for use in the workshop

Choosing the correct material

There are many different types of metals. We usually categorise metals into two types: **ferrous** and **non-ferrous**. Ferrous metals contain iron and non-ferrous metals contain no iron. There have been many recent developments with metal technology (**metallurgy**) so it is important to keep up to date when choosing the most appropriate material for the product you are making. Listed below is a decision chart that will help you choose the correct metal.

Ferrous metals

Non-ferrous metals

Items made from ferrous and non-ferrous metals

	METAL	PROPERTIES	USES
FERROUS	Mild steel	Malleable, ductile, strong, rusts easily	General engineering work, car bodies, structural frameworks
	High-speed steel	Harder than mild steel because of carbon content	Machine tools, drills
	Stainless steel	Hard and tough, nice appearance, high resistance to corrosion, expensive	Sinks, cutlery, knife blades
NON-FERROUS	Aluminium	Light, ductile, soft, high resistance to corrosion, silver colour	Car bodies, bicycle parts
	Brass	Strong, ductile, colourful, polishes well	Plumbing fittings, door furniture
	Copper	Malleable and ductile, good conductor of heat and electricity, polishes well	Water pipes, electrical wire
	Titanium	Very high strength/weight ratio, expensive	Engine components – performance cars, lightweight bicycle components

Preparing metal for use

Before we start work on metals we need to prepare the material for marking out (see next spread). Good preparation of the material allows it to be used safely and ensures accurate marking out.

Removing rough edges

The first process to make the metal safe is called **deburring** – taking burrs (rough edges) off the edges of the metal. To deburr the metal we use a file at an angle to the material. Be careful not to file at right angles to the edge of the material because this actually sharpens the edges.

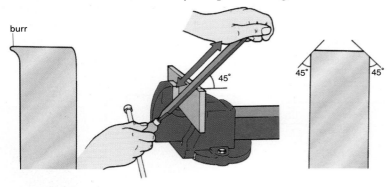

Preparing for bending

Sometimes when you have to bend a metal after marking out you will need to **anneal** the material first, that is, soften the metal by heating and then leaving to cool. We judge the heat of a metal by the colour change as it gets hotter. For information on recommended temperatures for annealing refer to preparing metals, Spread 4.12.

Cleaning and polishing

Another process that can be carried out before cutting or shaping is cleaning and polishing. Ferrous metals often arrive in the workshop covered with a film of grease to protect them from rusting. This can be removed by wiping with a rag soaked in white spirit or paraffin. To polish metals refer to Spread 4.13 on finishing metals.

If you are using sheet aluminium for some products it is possible to create a brushed effect using a wire brush in a power drill. You must be careful to ensure your work is clamped down to a bench or drill table.

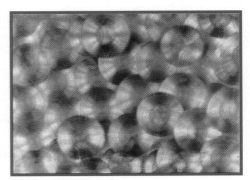

Polishing effects on metals

1 What are the advantages and disadvantages of choosing aluminium rather than steel for a bicycle wheel rim?

2 Outline the possible stages in preparing a piece of sheet metal for marking out.

3 Describe the processes needed before marking out a piece of sheet metal.

4.2 MARKING OUT METALS

BY THE END OF THIS SPREAD, YOU SHOULD BE ABLE TO:

- mark out metals ready for working
- identify tools used for marking out on metals

When marking out sizes and shapes on metals it is important that lines and marks show up clearly and are not rubbed out by mistake. Therefore, we often use tools and materials that are particular to metal and not used on wood or plastic. To enable our marking out to show up clearly on the metal we are using we often coat the metal in marking blue. This is an ink-based liquid that allows marks to show up clearly.

Achieving straight edges and square rulings

Before you start the marking-out process it is important that you establish the edges where you are going to begin taking accurate measurements from. These edges are called **datum edges** and should be checked for flatness and squareness using a **metal rule** or **engineer's square**.

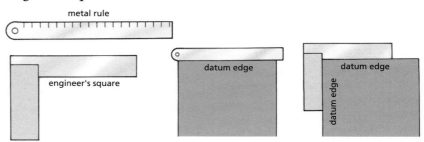

When we are marking lines on the metal we call this '**scribing a line**'; using a **scriber** to scratch the surface of the metal. The scriber is often used in conjunction with the following marking-out tools:

- an engineer's square for marking lines square to the datum edge or across a square material
- a metal rule for measuring distance away from the datum edge of a material.

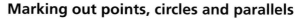

Marking out points, circles and parallels

To mark the positions of holes and other shapes we use a **centre punch**. The centre punch leaves a small indentation that can guide a drill or act as a centre for dividers.

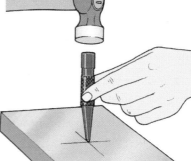

To mark out circles or arcs we use **dividers**. Mark out the centre for your circle or arc using a centre punch and then scribe the circle using the dividers.

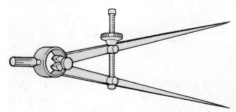

To mark a line parallel to the edge of a sheet or square material we use **odd-leg callipers**. This tool is designed so that one leg of the callipers is shaped to run along the edge of the material whilst the other leg scribes a parallel line.

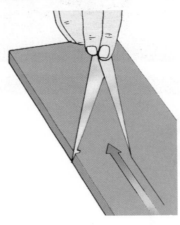

To mark out parallel lines on cylindrical and larger objects we use a **surface gauge** in conjunction with a **surface plate** and **angle block** or vee block.

1 Describe the method and tools used to mark out a circle on sheet metal.

2 Sketch two metal marking out tools and describe their uses.

3 Describe the use of datum edges when marking out.

4.3 CUTTING AND DRILLING METALS

By the end of this spread, you should be able to:

- select the correct tools and equipment to cut out metal shapes and remove waste materials

This spread shows the cutting and drilling tools we use on metals. These are not always the same tools as used for wood and plastic.

An industrial guillotine

TOOL		TASK	USEFUL TIPS
Hacksaw		For cutting straight lines in all metals	Ensure cutting blade has teeth facing forwards and is tight; a 'junior' hacksaw can be used for small objects
Tinsnips curved and straight		For cutting out shapes in sheet metals	Use straight snips for straight lines and external curves and curved snips for internal curved lines: nibble the material with short cuts rather than long cuts
Guillotine		For cutting straight lines in sheet metals	This machine is very dangerous; always make sure the guards are in place; line up your material and cut in short strokes
Piercing saw		For cutting intricate shapes out of sheet metals	Make sure your workpiece is held firmly on a bench pin – a device that supports the work whilst you are sawing; keep the saw moving with steady, even strokes

The drilling machine

The drilling machine is an invaluable piece of equipment. It allows you to drill accurate holes safely with the minimum of effort. It is particularly useful for drilling holes perpendicular to the top surface of the workpiece.

The drilling machine that you will find in the workshop is either called a **bench drill**, meaning it is bench-mounted, or a **pillar drill,** which is floor-mounted and allows larger workpieces to be drilled.

Holding your work

Always hold sheet metals in a **hand vice** or **mole grips**. Larger sections of metal should be held in a **machine vice**. If you are using drills over 8 mm diameter you should fasten the vice down to the bed of the drill using bolts.

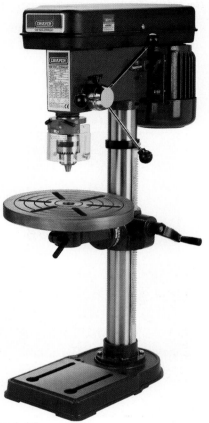

Bench drill

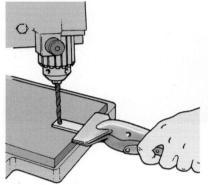

Holding your work using a bench vice or mole grips.

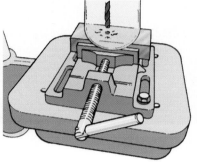

Holding your work using a vice that is bolted down to the bed of the drill.

Drilling holes to a certain depth

The **depth stop** mounted on the side of the drill allows you to set the depth of a hole and ensure the measurement is the same every time. One ring is locked against the other with a spring washer in between to stop them shaking loose.

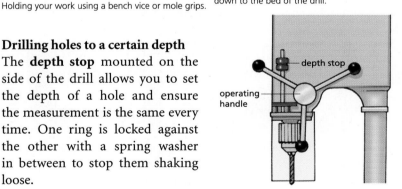

safety check:
Assess risk
Protective clothing
Eye protection
Extract fumes and dust
Guards in place

1 Describe the metalwork tools you would use to:
   a) cut out an aluminium disc
   b) cut a mild steel rod to length
   c) cut a heart-shaped hole into a copper pendant.

2 What are the advantages of using the pillar drill rather than a hand-held electric drill?

3 Sketch the depth stop on a pillar drill and explain its use.

4.4 TURNING AND MILLING METALS

BY THE END OF THIS SPREAD, YOU SHOULD BE ABLE TO:

- describe the centre lathe and its parts
- describe a milling machine

The centre lathe

The main use for the centre lathe in the school workshop is to cut cylindrical shaped objects or to centre drill. The **workpiece** is secured in the chuck and supported by the tailstock. The toolpost containing a **cutting tool** is moved along the lead screw to remove metal along the length of the workpiece. The **depth of cut** is adjusted by the cross slide which operates at 90 degrees to the lead screw.

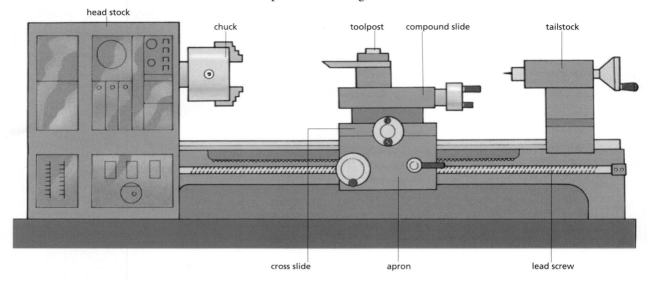

Lathe tools

There are different types of cutting tools that you can use on your workpiece. The diagram below shows different tools for different purposes.

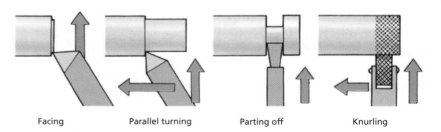

Facing   Parallel turning   Parting off   Knurling

The centre lathe can also be used to drill holes using a chuck mounted in the tailstock.

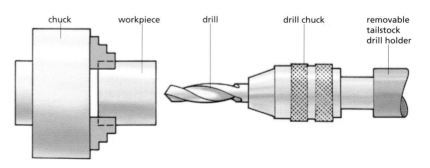

The milling machine

The most common milling machine found in school and college workshops is the **vertical milling machine**. This machine is used to cut slots and shapes out of blocks of metal. The milling cutter is held firmly in the head of the machine and then lowered into the metal whilst rotating. The bed of the machine (not the cutter) is then moved to machine slots or grooves in the workpiece.

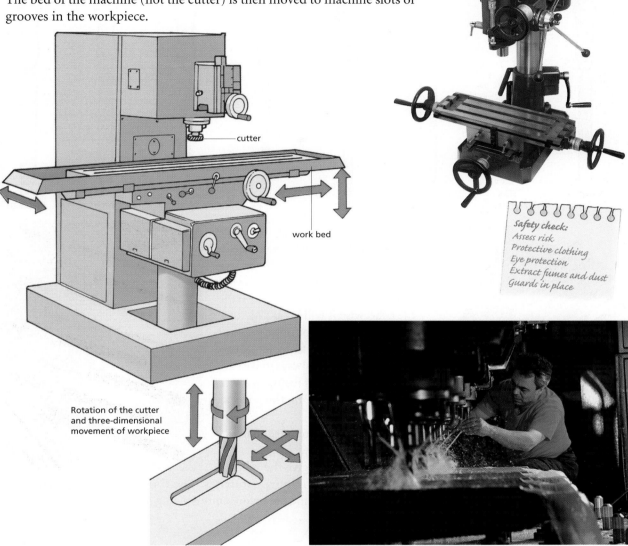

cutter

work bed

safety check:
Assess risk
Protective clothing
Eye protection
Extract fumes and dust
Guards in place

Rotation of the cutter and three-dimensional movement of workpiece

An industrial milling machine

1 Outline the safety precautions that should be observed when using the lathe and milling machine.

2 Sketch the lathe that you have in the school or college workshop and label the main parts.

3 Identify a turned component that has been made on a lathe and investigate the method of manufacture of each detail.

4.5 METAL SHAPING AND FORMING

- select the correct tools and equipment to shape and form metals
- understand industrial processes in shaping and forming metals

Filing metals

Metals can be shaped or formed using a variety of tools and processes. The most common tool for shaping metals is the **file**. There are a variety of shapes and tooth types of file. Here are the most commonly used file shapes:

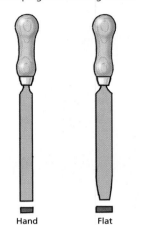     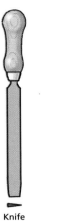

Hand Flat Half-round Round Square Three-square Knife Warding

For very fine or intricate work we use **needle files** which also come in a variety of shapes. These are delicate and expensive so be careful not to put too much pressure on the file otherwise it will break.

There are two common ways of filing metals: **cross filing** and **draw filing**. When filing always make sure the metal is secured firmly in a vice and as low down in the vice as possible.

We cross file to remove material quickly and roughly.

We draw file to give the metal a fine finish and to remove scratches. The finish can be made finer by rubbing chalk into the file before commencing draw filing.

Needle files

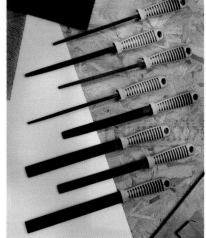

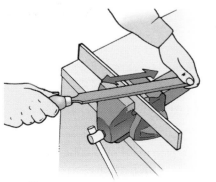

Cross filing

Draw filing

Bending metals

One of the useful qualities of metals is that they can be bent relatively easily. Sheet metal can be folded along lines or can be formed into shapes that are domed or hollow. To fold sheet metal along lines we can use **folding bars** or a **folding machine**.

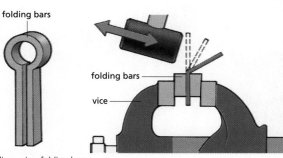

Folding using folding bars

To shape metals into domed or hollowed shapes we beat the metal. Beating is a method of shaping or forming a metal around a former using a mallet or hammer. The former can be made from a variety of materials depending on the metal and the effect required. Other methods of shaping metal involve the use of various types of bossing mallet with the metal resting on a soft base such as a sandbag.

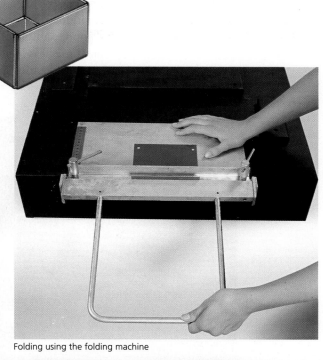

Folding using the folding machine

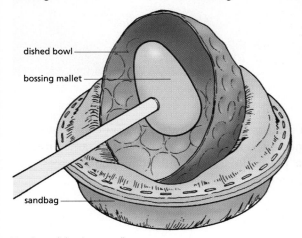

Forming a dish using a sandbag

Forming a dish shape using a wooden former or ring.

1 Draw and describe the uses of the metalwork files that you have available in your own school or college workshop.

2 Draw a development sketch of a sheet metal box to hold screws and describe the stages of manufacture using a folding machine.

4.6 PRESSING AND DIE-CASTING METAL

BY THE END OF THIS SPREAD, YOU SHOULD BE ABLE TO:

- select the correct tools and equipment to shape and form metals
- understand industrial processes in shaping and forming metals
- understand the term die-casting

Cold pressing

In industry companies will often need to form thin sheet metals into irregularly-shaped bodies or packages for their products. To do this they use industrial presses that press the metal into shape with enormous force. A good example of this is in the manufacture of car body panels. The thin sheet metal is loaded into a hardened **metal die** which is shaped top and bottom like the panel to be pressed.

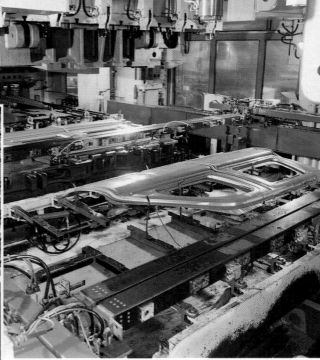

An industrial press

Pressed car door panels

An industrial press and die can also carry out other processes on the sheet metal at the same time. It can **pierce** holes and **indent** or **bend** shapes into the metal.

A pressed product

Pressing processes

piercing

bends

indented folds

Die-casting

This is a form of casting that uses metal dies or moulds into which molten metal is poured. Because of the high cost of manufacturing the dies that form the mouldings this process is only used when large quantity production is required. The metals that are cast in these dies are often zinc and aluminium alloys because they melt at relatively low temperatures and give accurate and low cost castings. Typical die-cast components would be metal toy cars and metal handles.

A die-cast model

The moulds split in two parts to enable the finished casting to be easily removed. The molten metal may be poured into the die by gravity or pressure fed into the die.

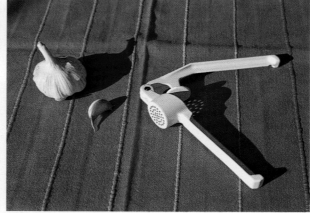

A die-cast garlic crusher

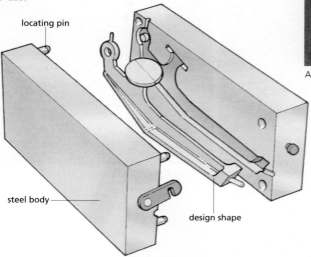

locating pin

steel body

design shape

---

1 Sketch a modern car and identify the main separate body panels that make up the structure of the car.

2 Give an example of a die-cast product and state what material it could be made from.

4.7 FORGING AND SAND-CASTING

BY THE END OF THIS SPREAD, YOU SHOULD BE ABLE TO:

- understand the term forging
- describe forging processes

Shaping metal by forging

Sometimes thin sections of ferrous and non-ferrous materials can be shaped cold, but thicker sections of iron and steel often have to be heated up before they can be bent. This process is called **forging**. To hot-forge metals we heat them up using a gas torch or by using a blacksmith's forge.

The metals that are used for forging are mild steel, wrought iron and tool steel. When these metals are red hot they are easy to bend and shape. The metal is placed into the heat of the fire or torch and heated to a red-hot state. It is then removed from the heat using tongs. The metal is then ready for shaping using a hammer and anvil or perhaps a large vice.

Below is a series of pictures that show the manufacture of a mild steel candle holder using different forging techniques.

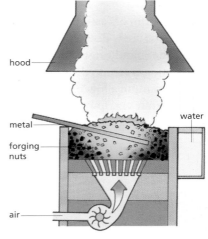

Blacksmith's forge

Producing a taper on the end of the candle holder

Safety check:
Assess risk
Protective clothing
Eye protection
Extract fumes and dust
Guards in place

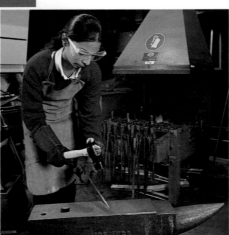

Putting a twist into the metal

Shaping a spiral into the stand of the candle holder

Casting

To cut down on shaping and forming in a very resistant material like metal it is possible to cast products. This has a number of advantages over **wasting** methods, that is methods that involve cutting away material to form the final shape. In the school or college workshop it is possible to cast with low melting point metals like aluminium and pewter.

There are different types of moulds for casting metals. You should be aware of sand-casting moulds used in your workshop and die-casting moulds used in industry (see page 65).

Sand-casting

Prepare the mould **pattern**. Make sure there is a **draft angle** on the pattern to allow easy withdrawal from the sand.

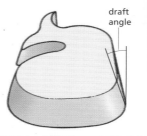

draft angle

The pattern is then placed on a baseboard and the bottom half of the flask which is called the **drag** is placed over the pattern. The drag is then filled with casting sand and levelled.

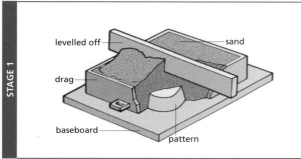

STAGE 1

levelled off — sand

drag

baseboard — pattern

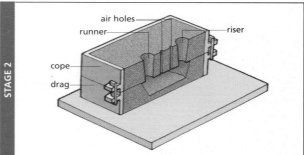

STAGE 2

air holes

runner — riser

cope

drag

The drag is then turned over with the baseboard attached. The **cope**, which is the top half of the flask, is now attached. The cope is then filled with sand to surround two formers called the **runner** and **riser**.

The runner and riser are now carefully removed and the two halves of the mould are separated. The pattern is removed and the cope and drag are put back together. The sand mould is now empty and ready to receive the molten metal.

STAGE 3

1 Give two reasons why a metal bar is best worked whilst red hot rather than cold.

2 Identify at least three products that could be made using sand casting.

3 Produce a flow chart that describes the method of producing a sand mould for casting.

4.8 JOINING METALS

- understand the difference between permanent and semi-permanent fastenings
- recognise different fasteners

There are many different ways of joining metals using permanent and semi-permanent methods. The method of joining depends on the material that is being joined and the purpose of the finished joint.

Listed below are different methods of joining metals including details of the materials they join and their most common use in industry.

PERMANENT JOINING METHODS AND TYPICAL APPLICATIONS	
JOINING METHOD	**TYPICAL APPLICATIONS**
RIVETS — Rivets	■ For joining sheet metals and plates ■ Fabrication of boxes and pivoting joints on tools such as wire strippers
Pop rivets	■ For joining thin sheet metals when one side of the join is inaccessible and for joining aluminium sheet because of difficulties with welding ■ Fabrication of boxes ■ Sheet aluminium frameworks
GLUE — Epoxy resin	■ For joining metal to metal or to other materials ■ Repairing broken metal products, joining plastic to metal, and to join metals when a gap is present
HOT JOINING — Soft soldering	■ For joining lightweight items and electrical components using alloy of lead and tin ■ Circuit boards; light-weight boxes
Silver soldering	■ For low temperature joining of metals, for example on brass using an alloy of silver, copper and zinc ■ For joining decorative tableware such as teapots and tankards
Brazing	■ For high strength joints using an alloy of copper and zinc ■ For joining steel bicycle frames
Welding	■ For high strength joints using a filler rod of similar material to the materials being joined ■ For joining steel tubing and heavy-duty fabrication work

NUTS, SCREWS AND BOLTS

SEMI-PERMANENT JOINING METHODS AND TYPICAL APPLICATIONS

JOINING METHOD	TYPICAL APPLICATIONS
Bolt and nut	▪ For holding two components together between head and nut ▪ For joining mechanisms and temporarily fixing metals
Cap head, hexagon socket screw	▪ For holding two components together; one component will be tapped to take screw ▪ Positioning of components on modern engineering assemblies: easy removal
Grub screw	▪ For holding wheels, pulleys on shafts ▪ Household appliance mechanisms
Stud	▪ Threaded both ends ▪ Engine components
Wing nut	▪ For finger tightening of components ▪ For products that are regularly disassembled
Ni-lock nut	▪ Shake-proof nut with oversized nylon insert ▪ For products that are subjected to vibrations and movement
Plain washer	▪ Used in conjunction with nut and bolt to distribute forces and stop damage to components being joined ▪ Most nut and bolt assemblies
Spring washer	▪ Shake-proof washer ▪ For products that are subjected to vibrations

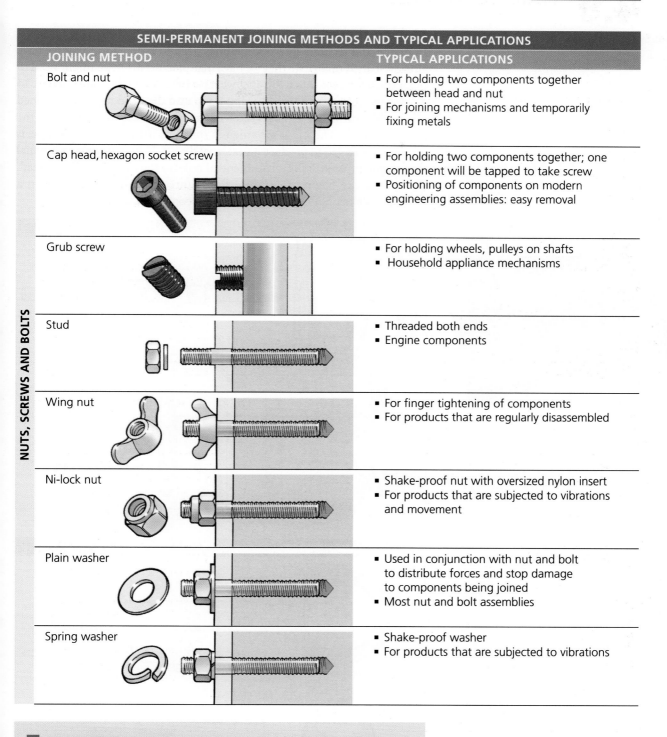

1 Disassemble a familiar product and identify fastenings that have been used in its assembly.

2 Look at a range of metal products and decide where they have been permanently joined and semi-permanently joined.

- produce a screw thread on a metal rod
- join sheet metal components by riveting

Making threads

In design and technology we sometimes need to fasten a rod that we have already shaped or an axle that we have manufactured. Or we might need to put a threaded hole into a product we have made to take a bolt or screw. To do this we cut a screw thread using a **tap and die**. The tap is a hardened screw with cutting teeth that is screwed into the correct size hole to cut the internal thread. The die is a hardened split nut with cutting teeth that is screwed onto a rod to produce an external thread. Before cutting an internal thread, you must drill the recommended hole for the corresponding thread. Before you can begin to cut an external thread you must file or turn a chamfer (see below) onto the rod of the recommended diameter.

AN INTERNAL SCREW THREAD

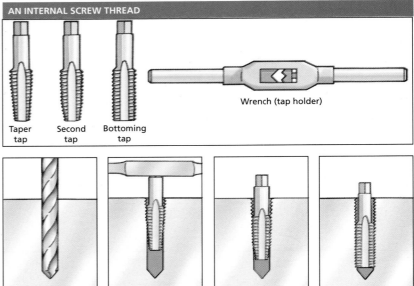

Taper tap   Second tap   Bottoming tap   Wrench (tap holder)

1 Tapping drill   2 Taper tap   3 Second tap   4 Bottoming tap

AN EXTERNAL SCREW THREAD

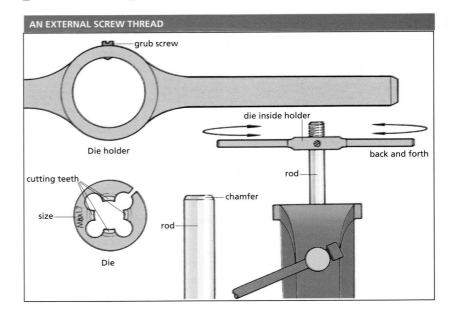

grub screw

Die holder

cutting teeth

size

Die

rod

die inside holder

back and forth

rod

chamfer

rod

Rivets

Sometimes we need to permanently join two metal sheet materials together and do not want to distort the materials through the use of hot joining methods. This is when we rivet the materials together. Riveted joints are also quite attractive if the process is carried out accurately and carefully. To improve appearance it is particularly important that holes for rivets are drilled in line and equally spaced. Shown below are two riveting methods: **plain rivets** and **pop rivets**.

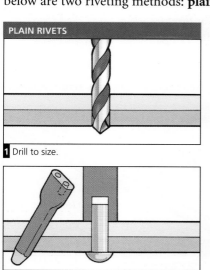

PLAIN RIVETS	POP RIVETING
1 Drill to size.	1 Drill to size.
2 Close the plates together using a rivet set.	2 Rivet is pushed into hole.
3 Hammer the head of the rivet to shape.	3 Rivet is squeezed using a rivet tool.
4 Finish the shape of the rivet using the rivet set.	4 The head snaps off leaving a riveted joint.

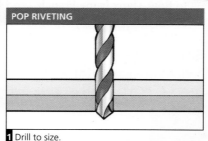

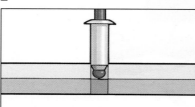

rivet tool

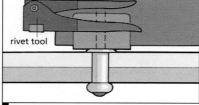

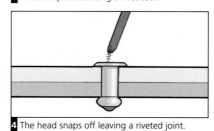

Two types of pop rivet gun. One has extended arms for greater leverage

1. Using a flow chart describe the method of producing a screw thread on a 8 mm diameter rod.

2. What are the advantages of riveting sheet metals rather than hot joining them?

71

4.10 SOLDERING AND BRAZING

BY THE END OF THIS SPREAD, YOU SHOULD BE ABLE TO:

- soft solder two metals together
- braze two metals together

Cleaning and fluxing

When we are carrying out any kind of hot joining of metals it is really important that the components are a good fit, are clean of dirt and grease and are temporarily held in place either in a vice or jig, or wired together. **Fluxes** are substances used when hot joining metals for the following reasons:

- ☐ They keep the metal clean and free of contamination.
- ☐ They break down the surface tension of the filler material enabling it to flow. (Flux is the French word for flow.)
- ☐ Some fluxes actually clean the metal being joined.

Soldering

Soft soldering is a method of joining two metals using low temperatures.

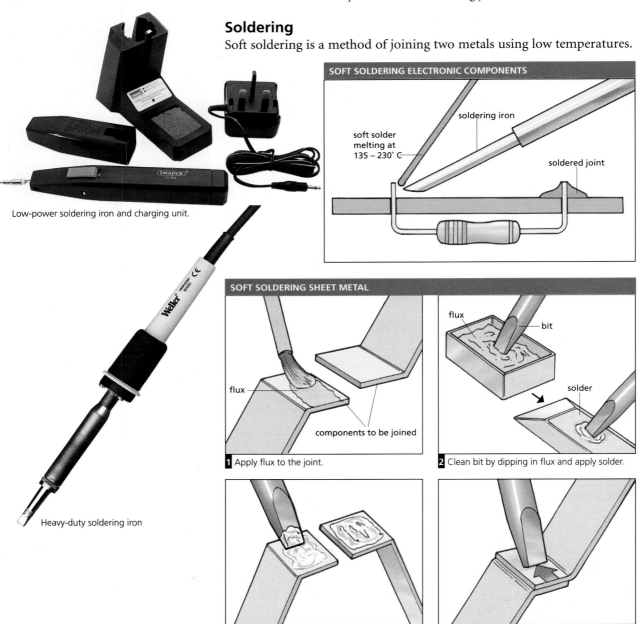

Low-power soldering iron and charging unit.

Heavy-duty soldering iron

SOFT SOLDERING ELECTRONIC COMPONENTS

soldering iron

soft solder melting at 135 – 230° C

soldered joint

SOFT SOLDERING SHEET METAL

flux

components to be joined

1 Apply flux to the joint.

flux

bit

solder

2 Clean bit by dipping in flux and apply solder.

3 Apply solder to both components.

4 Move tip of bit slowly along joint to heat solder.

Brazing

Brazing, or hard soldering, is a method of joining two metals together using high temperatures. It produces a very strong joint.

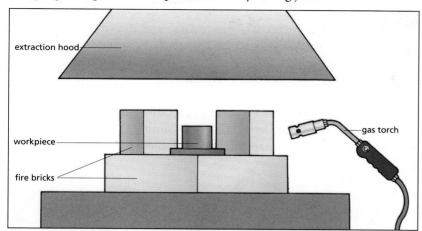

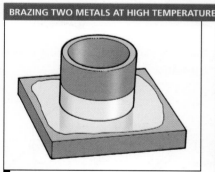

Brazing two metals is done at very high temperatures: 880–900°C. To create these high temperatures we need a brazing torch and hearth.

BRAZING TWO METALS AT HIGH TEMPERATURE

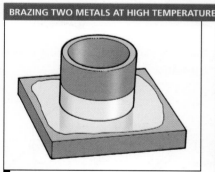

1 Ensure the two components are well fitting and are clean.

2 Mix flux powder with water until it forms a thin paste. Apply flux to the joint.

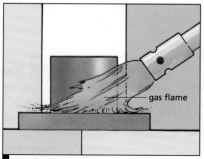

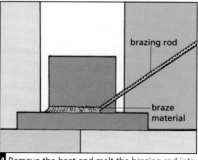

3 Heat the two components until red hot. Try to heat evenly throughout both components.

4 Remove the heat and melt the brazing rod into the joint.

> **1** What is the difference between soft soldering and hard soldering?
>
> **2** Make a chart that shows the different joining temperatures of soft and hard soldering and outline the steps for preparing the materials to be joined.

Safety check:
Assess risk
Protective clothing
Eye protection
Extract fumes and dust
Guards in place

When you have made a product from a metal you need to consider how the product could be manufactured in quantity. The processes of cold pressing and die-casting are for producing products in quantity but they often require sophisticated and expensive tooling. Outlined in this spread you will find different ways of producing products in quantity whilst maintaining quality.

Products made from sheet metal

If you have made a product from sheet metal there are a number of ways that you can maintain constant size and check for quality.

Produce a template from thin plywood or sheet aluminium to help you scribe out the shape of the development or net of your product.

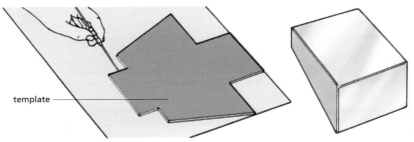

template

Produce a bending or measuring jig that will make manufacturing easier and check whether you are producing products of constant size.

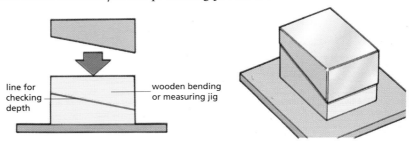

line for checking depth

wooden bending or measuring jig

Products made from tube, bar or rod

When you are making products from cylindrical or square metals you often need to cut the material to length accurately. This might involve making a cutting jig that could also include a checking template.

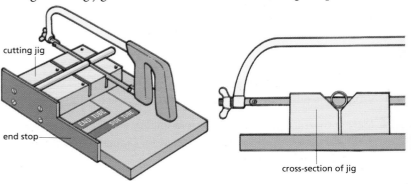

cutting jig

end stop

END TUBE   SIDE TUBE

cross-section of jig

Products forged from metal

Products that are hot or cold forged are often shaped into random shapes that are difficult to duplicate. Therefore it is a good idea to draw out a template of the desired shape or produce a three-dimensional checking jig of the shape.

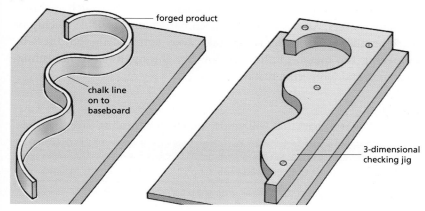

Products fabricated from metals and joined by heat

Frameworks made from tube, bar or rod that are welded or brazed together often require a jig to hold them in the correct position while joining.

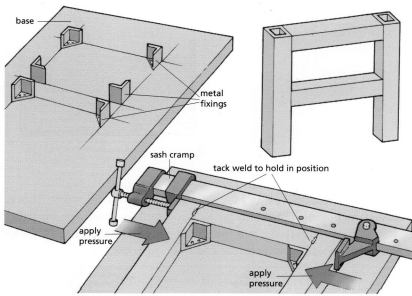

Welding or brazing jig

1 Disassemble a metal toy car and describe the processes used to manufacture each component in quantity.

2 Select a product you have made in metal and describe how the manufacturing process could be made easier and quicker by using jigs and templates for mass production.

In Spread 4.1 we looked at the preparation of metals by **annealing**. This is the process of softening the metal by heating to a specific temperature to change the structure and therefore the behaviour of that metal. There are other heat treatments that can be carried out on metals to change their behaviour. **Hardening** a metal makes it more resistant to denting and scratching, which is particularly useful when making tools such as chisels and screwdrivers. After a metal has been hardened it is liable to chip or break because it is brittle, so we take away some of the hardness by **tempering** the metal. Outlined below are the methods of annealing, hardening and tempering metals.

Annealing

Listed below is a chart that will guide you when annealing sheet metals:

COLOUR	TEMPERATURE	METHOD
Steel	Heat to cherry red (725°C)	Cool slowly in sand
Aluminium	Coat in soap, heat until soap turns black (400°C)	Cool slowly
Brass	Heat to dull red (500°C)	Cool slowly
Copper	Heat to dull red	Cool slowly

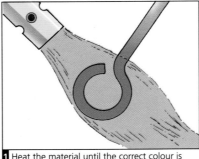

1 Heat the material until the correct colour is achieved.

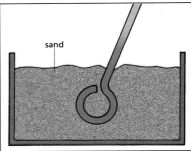

2 Place the material in sand so that it can cool very slowly.

Hardening

Hardening is achieved by plunging the item into cold water. This is called **quenching**. Often only the working surfaces need to be hardened so it is advisable not to quench the whole object. Otherwise the handles of some objects will become brittle and fracture in use.

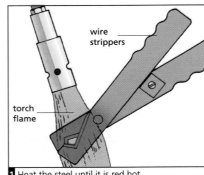

1 Heat the steel until it is red hot.

2 Quench the steel in water.

Tempering

After steel has been hardened it is often brittle. To make the steel tougher and less likely to break we re-heat the steel to carry out the tempering process.

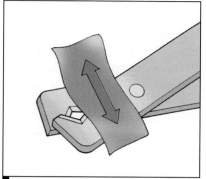

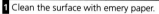
1 Clean the surface with emery paper.

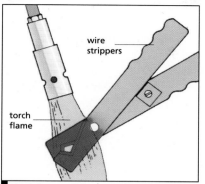
2 Gently heat until the material is the correct tempering colour.

3 Quench in water.

COLOUR	TEMPERATURE	USES
Brown/purple	260°C	Punches
Purple	270°C	Press tools
Dark purple	280°C	Cold chisels Scewdrivers Wirecutters

Industrial processes

During manufacturing of mass-produced products, processes such as welding might change the working properties of the materials used. If this happens the products need to be heat-treated after assembly.

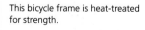
This bicycle frame is heat-treated for strength.

1 Why do we need to heat treat some metal products?

2 Describe the stages in heat treating a screwdriver that has been made in the school or college workshop.

4.13 FINISHING METALS

The final finish that is applied to a metal product is often both to protect and improve the appearance of the product. Before the finishing process can begin it is important that the metal is thoroughly cleaned of grease and grime. There are a number of finishes that are available to the designer.

Finishing papers

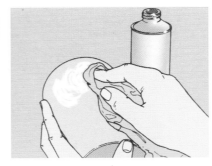

Hand polishing

Initial finishing can be carried out by draw filing across the metal surface and then using emery cloths of increasing grades to polish the surface. An abrasive polish is then applied to a cloth and the surface is polished using circular movements.

Machine polishing

A polishing machine has mops or buffers attached to a rotating wheel. Abrasive polish is applied to the polishing wheel and the product is then carefully pressed against the wheel until the required surface finish is required. It is important that the workpiece is kept within the safe working area of the wheel and that no loose clothing comes into contact with the moving parts.

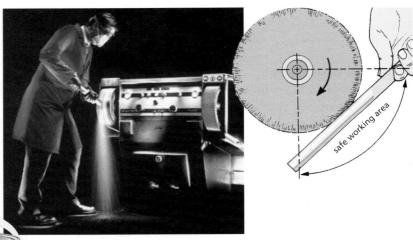

safe working area

Painting

Metal paints come in a wide variety of colours and textures. When choosing a paint finish it is very important that you check the product's suitability for use on metals. Some paint finishes require a rustproof undercoat whilst others protect the surface with a single coating. It is possible to obtain a specialised hammered finish or a metallic finish.

Dip coating

This finishing method gives a very waterproof **plastic coating** to the metal and can also be used as a handle finish for manufactured tools. The coating is available in clear and a wide range of colours. The metal product is heated in an oven to approximately 180°C. The product is then plunged into a fluidised bath of polystyrene powder and immediately the powder begins to stick to the metal. Hold it in the tank for at least 5 seconds. The product is removed and excess powder is shaken into the bath. The product must then be hung by wire to continue the melting and drying process.

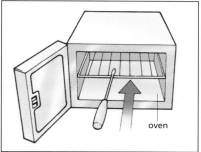

1 Product to be coated placed in oven and heated to approximately180°C.

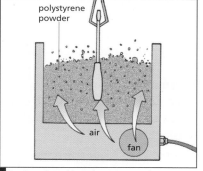

2 Product dipped in polystyrene powder.

Safety check:
Assess risk
Protective clothing
Eye protection
Extract fumes and dust
Guards in place

Enamelling

Enamelling is often used in the workshop to improve the appearance of a product, particularly jewellery. In industry it is used to protect products such as cookers, washing machines and bicycle frames. The process uses powdered glass that is melted onto the surface of the metal in an enamelling oven. Additional colours can be added to the surface later, and different textures created by using larger grains of glass.

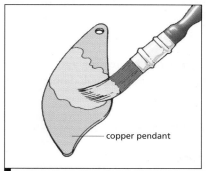

1 Brush pendant with wallpaper paste.

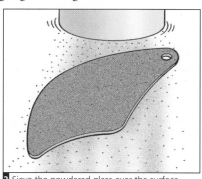

2 Sieve the powdered glass over the surface.

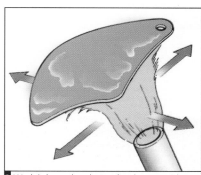

3 Work is heated underneath using a gas/air torch until the glass melts.

1 State a finishing process that could be applied to the following metal components:
   a) a metal gate
   b) a garden swing
   c) the handle of a pair of electrical pliers.

5.1 CHOOSING AND MARKING OUT ON PLASTICS

BY THE END OF THIS SPREAD, YOU SHOULD BE ABLE TO:

- identify various plastics
- describe and the qualities plastics offer the designer
- know the issues involved in marking out plastic sheet

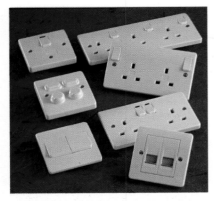

Types of plastic

There are two main types of plastic: **thermosetting plastics** and **thermoplastics**. All plastics are synthetic and derive originally from oil or sometimes coal. There are hundreds of different types of plastic each with a unique combination of qualities. New plastics are being made all the time which have the exact qualities the designer has specified. Qualities can be altered using the following powdered **additives**:

- Plasticisers which make the plastic more bendy
- Antistatics to cut down the static electricity the plastic can carry
- Antioxidants to reduce the degradation when exposed to air or UV light
- Flame retardants which make the plastic more heat resistant
- Pigments which change the colour and pattern of the plastic
- Fillers which make the plastic stronger.

Thermosetting plastics

Once made into shape these cannot be re-formed. They are brittle and hard and can be prone to cracking if twisted or knocked. They are heat-resistant.

	NAME OF PLASTIC	PROPERTIES	ITEMS MADE	OTHER NOTES
THERMOSETTING PLASTICS	Used in schools and colleges			
	Polyester resin	Thick clear liquid – used for coating or mixing with glass for reinforced plastic (GRP)	Canoes/paper-weights	Irritant, wear barrier cream
	Epoxy resin	Liquid – made into two-part glues	Gluing and potting products	Also used for surface coating/laminating
	Used in industry			
	Urea formaldehyde	Usually white, tough, brittle	Electronic fittings	Also made into Cascamite glue
	Phenol formaldehyde	Dark, hard, very brittle, resists heat	Pan handles	If overheated gives off toxic fumes

Thermoplastics

These are sensitive to heat; they can be reformed by heating and will tend to return to their original shape if they can; over-heating will damage their chemical structure.

	NAME OF PLASTIC	PROPERTIES	ITEMS MADE	OTHER NOTES
THERMOPLASTICS	Used in schools and colleges			
	Acrylic	Scratches easily, formed into shapes using many methods	Baths; spectacle lenses	Also called polymethyl-metacrylate (PMMA)
	High/low density polythene	Tough when formed; can be flow moulded, injection moulded, extruded	Injection moulded model aeroplanes; bottles; buckets	High density called HDPE
			Plastic bags; wire insulation	Low density called LDPE
	Nylon	Stiff, strong, self-lubricating	Bearings; mechanical components	Difficult to join with glues
	High impact polystyrene	Easily formed, retains shape	Open hollow shapes of all sizes	Also called HIPS

	NAME OF PLASTIC	PROPERTIES	ITEMS MADE	OTHER NOTES
	Used in industry			
THERMOPLASTICS	Polyethylene teraphthalate	Tough and clear plastic	Drink bottles, including baby bottles	Called PET
	Polypropylene	Very flexible and resists cracking and tearing even though thin	Yoghurt pots; margarine tubs; crisp packets	Called PP
	Polyvinyl chloride	Very strong and flexible; weatherproof	Gutters/window frames	Called PVC; affected by UV light which makes it brittle
	Acrylonitrile butadiene styrene	Very strong; scratch-resistant	Household products; cameras; kettles; vacuum cleaners	Called ABS

Marking out

Of the four common plastics used in schools and colleges, only acrylic and high impact polystyrene are used in sheet form (the others come as powder or liquid) and require marking out before use. **Acrylic sheet** comes with a thin protective material covering it which can be plastic or paper. This is to avoid scratches which are really difficult to remove completely. Consequently the protection is kept in place as long as the process allows. Whilst it is in place, ordinary pencils can be used to mark out. However, if it is removed, a chinagraph pencil or special spirit-based pen is needed. If the marking out precedes drilling then a piece of masking tape is stuck over the area first. This allows the marking to be seen clearly and also stops the drill slipping across the plastic surface. This procedure is also used if the plastic is to be cut using a thin blade or on a machine with a blade that moves very fast. The tape in this case stops the plastic getting too hot during cutting. If it does get too hot it tends to weld itself back together.

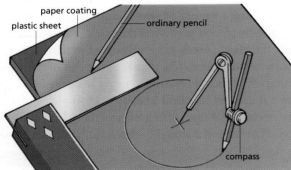

Marking a circle with protective coating.

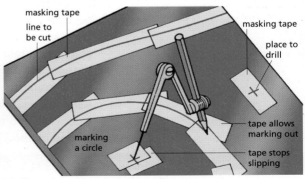

Marking a circle without protective coating.

1 Why do operators stick masking tape onto plastic sheeting before cutting out with a coping saw?

2 Which plastic is used to make crisp packets and why?

3 If you were given the task of designing and making a plastic toy, which plastic would you choose and why?

5.2 CUTTING OUT PLASTICS

By the end of this spread, you should be able to:

- understand which tools and techniques to use when cutting plastics

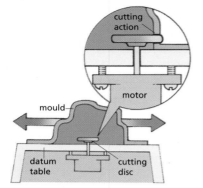

As plastics can be moulded and formed into new shapes when heated, the most common reason for wanting to cut plastics is to remove the waste around a moulded shape.

Cutting round moulded plastic

After vacuum forming using either acrylic, or more likely, high impact polystyrene, the waste has to be cut away. It is difficult to achieve a good quality of cut using hand tools because of difficulties gaining access and holding the work. A very useful machine has been designed which uses a fibrous disc (which will not cut fingers) that spins at high speed. This can be adjusted to any height above the datum table and allows mouldings to be trimmed at a constant height.

Using acrylic sheet

In the workshop acrylic sheets are used in many colours and thicknesses. They are very versatile and can be used flat or moulded using a whole range of techniques. Once its thin plastic or plastic protective layer is removed an acrylic sheet is very brittle and may crack if twisted or bent. This brittleness must be remembered when cutting acrylic as it is easy to snap if it is not supported properly.

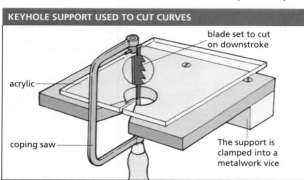

KEYHOLE SUPPORT USED TO CUT CURVES

Curves and difficult shapes

In the diagram a special 'keyhole' support has been made to support the plastic when cutting with a coping saw. This is the best way to cut difficult curves or intricate shapes.

Cutting straight lines

Straight lines can be cut using a variety of saws including tenon saws and hacksaws. Acrylic can also be planed providing the blade is shaped and set at a low cut rate. Again the plastic needs to be supported so that the action of the plane does not twist the plastic. The plastic at the end of the stroke is vulnerable to splitting off. This can be avoided using a waste piece of the same material clamped at the end (method 1 below), or simply by planing from each end to the middle and then lifting off (method 2 below). The second method is less accurate and a straight edge is difficult to achieve.

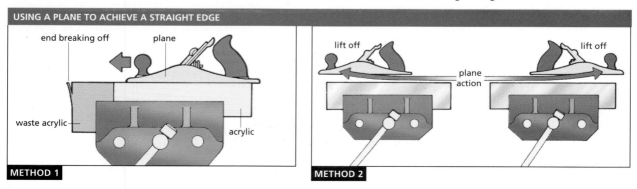

USING A PLANE TO ACHIEVE A STRAIGHT EDGE

METHOD 1

METHOD 2

Drilling holes

The brittleness of the material also has to be taken into account when drilling holes into plastic. First the twist drill tip has to be reground to give a shallower angle. This reduces stress on the bottom edge of the plastic as the drill nears the end of its cut. Holes larger than 6 mm diameter cannot be drilled in one stage. It is best to start with a pilot drill, say a 3 mm, and then build up in 2 or 3 mm steps.

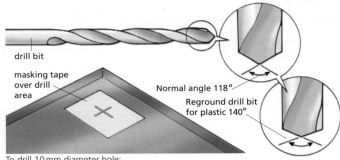

drill bit

masking tape over drill area

Normal angle 118°

Reground drill bit for plastic 140°

To drill 10 mm diameter hole:
Step 1 – drill 3 mm hole   Step 2 – drill 8 mm hole   Step 3 – drill 10 mm hole

Scoring and breaking

Many plastics can be snapped down a straight line, although this is a rough method and best attempted with thin polystyrene or ABS. To do this the plastic is first weakened down the line of cut by scoring. Once scored the plastic is placed along a straight edge and supported using a long metal rule. Larger pieces may need clamping over the edge using G-clamps. It is possible to break off smooth curves but sharp curves and complex shapes are best cut, not broken.

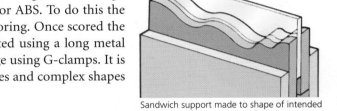

Sandwich support made to shape of intended cut stops bending and therefore cracking.

Cleaning up using a file

After cutting, the plastic often has very untidy edges which contrast with the very shiny surfaces top and bottom. Metalwork files of any size can be used to shape the edge accurately and begin the cleaning process. Small needle files can be used to achieve very fine detail. Care must be taken if a cross filing technique is used. Draw filing is much less likely to crack the plastic. To achieve an even better quality finish, you can use abrasive papers, including 'wet and dry' and an abrasive polish.

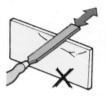

Cross filing will damage the plastic.

Draw filing will not damage the plastic.

Using machine tools

Great care must be taken when cutting plastic with a machine due to the additional risk of heat. A machine fret saw has a very thin blade which gets very hot when cutting. This tends to fuse the two pieces of plastic back together again as it passes through. This can be avoided by first sticking masking tape over the line of the cut and also slowing the speed of the blade and the speed at which the material is passed under the blade.

1 What difficulties might you face when working with acrylic, and how are they overcome? Give 3 examples.

2 How and why do we alter the tip of a twist drill when drilling acrylic sheet?

3 Explain all the steps in the process of drilling a 12 mm hole in a piece of acrylic plastic if you were given standard drill bits. Use a flow chart to explain all the elements of the process.

5.3 SHAPING AND FORMING PLASTICS (I)

BY THE END OF THIS SPREAD, YOU SHOULD BE ABLE TO:

- understand how to form thermoplastics using a range of techniques

Forming thermoplastics

Forming sheets of thermoplastic material is easy because at relatively low temperatures it becomes very flexible and will stretch a long way before breaking. There are various methods which can be used to form shapes using common plastics like acrylic or high impact polystrene.

Bending along a line

Bending along a straight line can be achieved using a simple machine called a **strip heater**. The machine has a long thin heater element which warms the plastic along the line of the required bend. Once the plastic has become flexible, due to the localised heating, it is placed on a former to keep it in shape whilst it cools and solidifies.

1 Mark line using a chinagraph pencil or spirit-based pen.

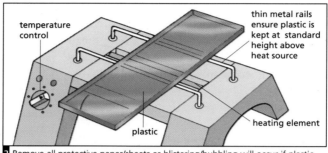

temperature control

thin metal rails ensure plastic is kept at standard height above heat source

plastic

heating element

2 Remove all protective paper/sheets as blistering/bubbling will occur if plastic gets too hot. Always use heat-proof gloves to hold plastic. Wait until cold before removing.

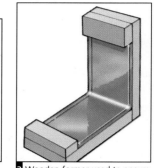

3 Wooden former used to ensure correct shape. A small amount of rounding will occur. Wait until cold before removing.

Press forming

If a more complex, three-dimensional shape is required then press forming is a quick but not very accurate method which might be appropriate. This method uses a two-part mould to sandwich the hot plastic (160–180°C) in between. Pressure is applied using clamps and the plastic left to cool. Once the plastic has cooled to room temperature the clamps can be removed.

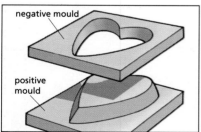

negative mould

positive mould

1 Cut out negative mould shape, larger than mould with slightly sloping sides. Fit positive shape to solid base.

2 Place plastic sheet on foil tray. Heat at 160–180°C for 10 minutes.

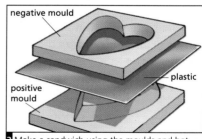

negative mould

plastic

positive mould

3 Make a sandwich using the moulds and hot plastic.

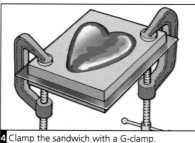

4 Clamp the sandwich with a G-clamp.

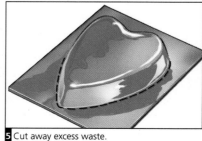

5 Cut away excess waste.

Plastic memory

Besides becoming flexible when heated, thermoplastic also has the unique quality of trying to return to its original shape. This 'memory' can be used in the production of some exciting pieces. See the steps below.

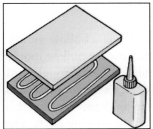

1 Stick together 2 colours of plastic using Tensile 12 or another plastic glue. Heat the plastic.

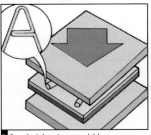

2 Sandwich wire mould between heavy blocks and *hot* plastic. Apply strong pressure.

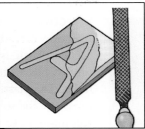

3 Allow to cool. Take out wire mould and remove surplus top colour using a file.

4 Place back in oven at 180°. Mould shape will mysteriously rise above base shape.

Vacuum forming

Thermoplastics of various sorts and thicknesses can be formed into quite complex shapes using a **vacuum former**. First a mould is made. In order for the moulding to be removed after forming the sides must be sloping. The angle of the slope is called the **draft**. Air holes can be drilled to prevent air pockets forming when the vacuum is turned on. The vacuum pulls the plastic so tightly over the mould that it is often difficult to remove it. The thickness of the plastic will dictate the height of the moulding which can be formed. Webbing will occur if the shape is too tall.

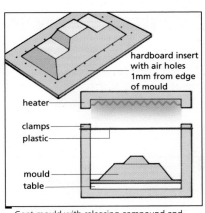

hardboard insert with air holes 1mm from edge of mould

heater

clamps
plastic

mould
table

Coat mould with releasing compound and attach to hardboard insert.

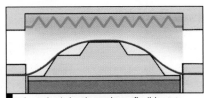

When plastic has heated to a flexible state, raise table to place mould in plastic.

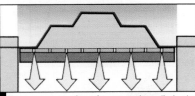

3 Turn on vacuum for a few seconds until plastic adopts the exact shape of mould. If mould is tall you may need to blow the plastic into a dome before raising the mould.

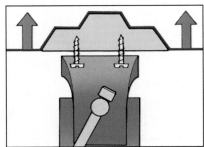

4 To remove a tight moulding, drill 2 holes in the mould, then put in screws and hold screw heads in metal vice and pull plastic. Use a fibrous disc cutter to cut away waste as in Spread 5.2.

1   What causes webbing in vacuum forming?

2   Design a souvenir for a theme park of your choice which could be made using plastic memory properties.

3   Draw a flow diagram to explain how to use a vacuum forming machine. Use the information in Spread 7.1 to help you.

5.4 SHAPING AND FORMING PLASTICS (II)

- understand the advantages and disadvantages of three more techniques
- select the one most suitable as a solution to a design problem

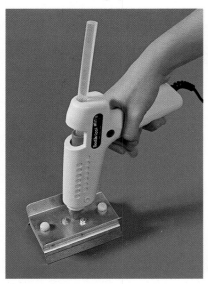

There are other methods of making one-off prototypes using plastic products. The following ways of shaping plastics are used less often than those on the preceding pages. This is due to a combination of factors like safety, skill requirements, and cost.

Injection moulding

Injection moulding produces solid plastic shapes using a hollow mould. Melted plastic is injected through the **sprue hole** into the hollow mould until it fills all the cavity. The air from the mould escapes through **vent holes**. The plastic is cooled and the two halves of the mould are separated to release the solid plastic shape. The simplest way of demonstrating this technique is to use a hot glue gun to melt a coloured glue stick. The diagram illustrates how a simple mould can be made using MDF. Silicon spray is a good releasing agent which will stop the plastic adhering to the mould.

INJECTION MOULDING USING A GLUE GUN

1 Spray mould with silicon and clamp tightly together.

2 Dispense molten plastic into sprue hole. Goggles must be worn.

INJECTION MOULDING MOULD

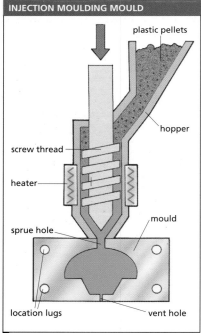

1 The screw thread rotates to inject the molten plastic down through the machine.

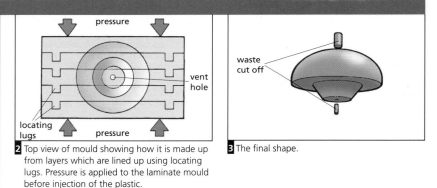

2 Top view of mould showing how it is made up from layers which are lined up using locating lugs. Pressure is applied to the laminate mould before injection of the plastic.

3 The final shape.

A small injection moulder is an expensive machine. Making moulds is usually very difficult unless a layered, or **laminated** mould is made.

The plastic (in pellet form) is placed in the hopper at the top of the machine. Using a gravity feed, the pellets drop into a heated barrel which melts the plastic. It is then injected into the mould. As soon as the plastic has cooled a little, the parts of the mould are separated and the shape is produced. The only finishing needed is to cut off the waste plastic at the sprue holes and vents. If the mould is worn there may be a little leakage of plastic where the layers of the mould are pushed together. This is called **flash** which has to be removed from the moulded component if it is unsightly.

Glass-reinforced plastic (GRP)

GRP can be used to make large, hollow shapes which are extremely strong, like canoes or boat hulls. However, shaping it is a long and difficult process requiring careful measurement and mixing of chemicals, all of which carry a variety of health warnings. Protective barrier cream must be worn and extraction of fumes is essential. GRP is rarely used in schools and colleges.

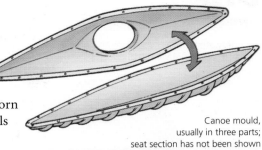

Canoe mould, usually in three parts; seat section has not been shown

USING GLASS-REINFORCED PLASTIC TO MAKE A CANOE

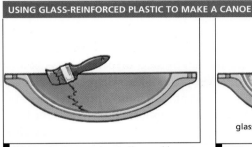

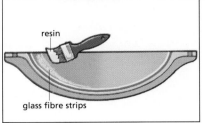

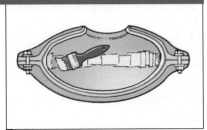

1 Paint a releasing agent on to the mould.

2 Add several layers of glass fibre strips and resin.

3 Put all parts of the mould together and use resin to join the parts. Release the mould and polish.

Casting using resin

Casting with resin is a safer technique. It is useful for producing large solid objects. There are a variety of ways to make a mould. If you want to make a resin copy of a solid object, then the object itself can be used in making the mould. This technique is used when making model skeletons for educational use (see below). If you want to cast a new design you start by making a clay model. Coat the object or model with layers of latex rubber. When dry, peel off the rubber mould and fill with a mixture of casting resin, pigment and hardener. When set, peel off the latex until the mould disintegrates.

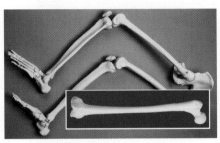

Resin models of bones

CASTING USING PLASTIC RESIN IN A LATEX MOULD

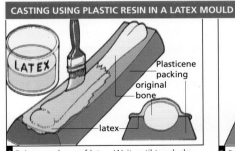

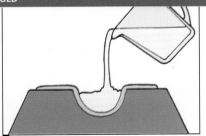

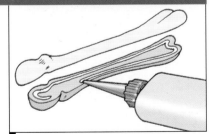

1 Paint on a layer of latex. Wait until touch dry, repeat until 20 layers have been built up. Leave overnight to cure.

2 Peel off latex negative mould. Turn over and support with more Plasticine. Fill with resin mixed with hardener and pigment.

3 Repeats the process with the other half of the bone. Stick the two halves together using Tensol 12.

1 If you were asked to make a chair seat especially for a disabled person, which forming technique would you use and how would you do it?

2 Which technique would be best to use if you were making a small batch of plastic chess pieces to your own design?

5.5 JOINING PLASTICS

BY THE END OF THIS SPREAD, YOU SHOULD BE ABLE TO:

- identify which adhesive to use and how to use it to join a variety of plastics

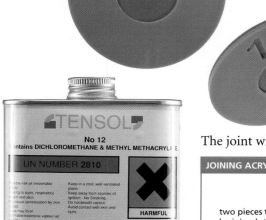

Joined acrylic

Safety guidance on Tensol

Safety check:
Assess risk
Protective clothing
Eye protection
Extract fumes and dust
Guards in place

Plastics can be joined permanently, using adhesives or tapes, and semi-permanently using fastenings.

Using adhesives

A **solvent adhesive** actually melts the two surfaces of plastic to be joined. When it evaporates away the plastic hardens again, making a permanent bond. The strength of all of these joints depends on the surface area of the contact between the two pieces to be joined. A small surface area gives a weak joint and a large area a strong joint. It is very important to press joining surfaces together properly to exclude air and maximise the strength of the bond. The diagram below shows how to join two pieces of acrylic or ABS using a liquid solvent. The joint is prepared dry and then the solvent is applied. It seeps into the joint using capillary action and then evaporates quickly. The joint will be up to full strength 10 minutes after the final coat.

JOINING ACRYLIC USING A LIQUID SOLVENT

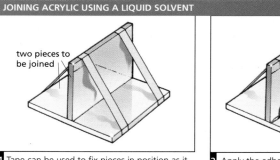

two pieces to be joined

1 Tape can be used to fix pieces in position as it does not mark the surface.

2 Apply the adhesive using either a fine brush or a pipette.

For larger jobs a thicker glue called Tensol 12 is needed. This also works by temporarily melting the plastic. Its thicker consistency allows accurate application over a wider area. This is done using a brush. The area either side of the joint needs to be protected using masking tape so the adhesive does not damage the nearby surface. This would be very difficult to tidy up.

JOINING ACRYLIC PLASTIC USING TENSOL 12

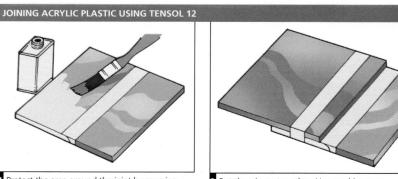

1 Protect the area around the joint by covering with masking tape. Apply Tensol 12 with a brush.

2 Put the pieces together. Use masking tape to fix the position while the adhesive dries.

Joining using tape

Double-sided tapes are an excellent way to join plastics. Recent developments in adhesives technology have made these tapes as strong as other glues, providing the surface they are to stick is properly cleaned.

JOINING PLASTIC USING DOUBLE-SIDED TAPE

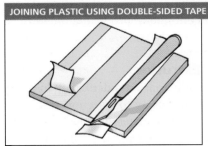
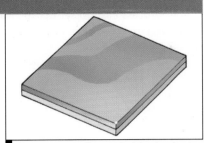

1 Clean both surfaces using methylated spirit. Stick down the tape trimming ends accurately. Peel off the backing.

2 Always ensure surfaces to be joined are kept clean. Assemble with care as the pieces will instantly fix. Should only be done once.

Semi-permanent fixing of plastic

Plastic sheets can be joined using a whole variety of fixings which can be undone and then repositioned. Plastic rivets work in a similar way to metal rivets. The rivets come in two parts but can only be joined once as they have a serrated shaft which allows movement in only one direction.

Plastic rivet

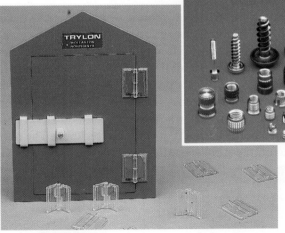

Fixings for plastic

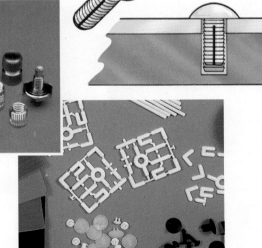

1 Why do you tape the edges of a piece of acrylic that you're joining using Tensol 12?

2 Draw out the process you would use to glue the six sides of a cube together using a liquid solvent glue.

5.6 PLASTIC MANUFACTURING IN QUANTITY

BY THE END OF THIS SPREAD, YOU SHOULD BE ABLE TO:

- identify the method used to mass manufacture several different forms of plastic

Injection moulding is a technique used in both workshops and industry. Industrial machines, however, bear little resemblance to the manually operated ones found in small workshops. The major differences are that the machines are fully adjustable, automatic and have water cooling channels running through the mould. These factors combine to make the whole process easy to set up and run continually, producing the finished items at a very fast rate.

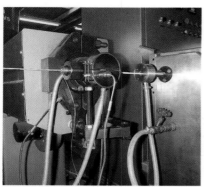

An industrial plastic extruder

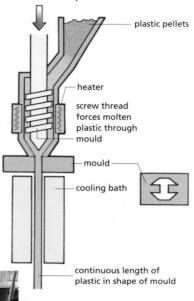

plastic pellets

heater

screw thread forces molten plastic through mould

mould

cooling bath

continuous length of plastic in shape of mould

Extrusion

Industrial **extruders** work in a very similar way to injection moulders. The raw material is the same range of pelleted plastics, placed into a hopper and heated. The hot plastic is forced down a long barrel using a rotating screw thread. The barrel is heated using bands along its length. The material is then squeezed through a small shaped hole, or die. This produces a continuous length of plastic of a uniform cross-section with the same profile as the die. A good example of this would be an extruded curtain rail.

Extrusion blow moulder

This is a variation on the extrusion process which is used to make plastic drinks bottles. A normal extrusion method is used to make a tube of hot plastic. This is fed into a hollow mould which closes on the bottom of the tube. This seals the tube so when air is pumped into the middle of the tube the plastic expands to take the shape of the mould. The walls of the section of extruded tube have been cleverly shaped and are thicker where the bottle is widest. This ensures the finished bottle has walls of constant thickness. The only finishing is to cut off the surplus plastic called the **flashing** or **flash**.

Bottles being made using an extrusion blow moulder.

EXTRUSION BLOW MOULDING

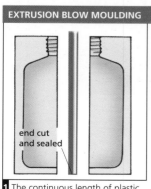

end cut and sealed

1 The continuous length of plastic is cut and sealed and placed into the mould.

2 The mould is shut.

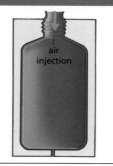

air injection

3 Air is blown into the plastic so that it fills and takes on the shape of the mould.

flashing

flashing

4 The shape is cooled and the flashing cut off.

Calendering

Calendering is used to shape thermoplastic materials into sheet or thin film. Plastic pellets are heated in a hopper and passed between heated rollers to produce a sheet. The thickness of the sheet is controlled by adjusting the distance between the last pair of rollers. The plastic is then cooled in a water bath before being rolled up on spools at the end of the machine.

Thin plastic sheeting being made with a calendering machine.

Rotational moulding

Rotational moulding is the technique used to make large, hollow, thick-walled items like water tanks or dustbins from polythene. The plastic is put into the mould in powder form. The walls of the mould are then heated and rotated. As the powder touches the hot walls it forms a skin. This builds up until all the plastic is a constant thickness. Rotation continues whilst the mould is then cooled to harden the plastic.

Rotational moulding

Compression moulding

Saucepan handles are commonly made using compression moulding. The mould is made in two halves which are heated using steam or electricity. Plastic in powder, pellet or bead form is fed into the mould which is closed under pressure. As the powder softens it is forced into all of the mould. Once cool the plastic sets hard. The two halves of the mould are then parted to release the finished item, and the process starts again.

Handles made by compression moulding

1 Describe extrusion moulding using sketches.

2 Which method of manufacture would be used to make a thin film of plastic?

3 Explain how an industrial injection moulder varies from the glue gun example described in Spread 5.4.

5.7 FINISHING PLASTIC PRODUCTS

- achieve a good quality finish on all types of plastic
- apply several different types of finish

The word 'finish' does not simply mean to complete the manufacture of an object. In technology we use this word to define the whole of the last manufacturing process. This phase starts when the item has been assembled and can be a very lengthy process depending upon the methods used. When using plastics however, this is often quite a short job. This is because we often mould or form plastic, and this process gives a good surface finish. The only part which may need some attention is the edge where the waste or flashing has been removed.

Finishing edges

The edge of a piece of acrylic is first finished using files. A rough grade of file can be used at first, followed by increasingly smooth files to improve the finish. The small scratches which the files leave behind can be removed using a fine grade silicon carbide paper (or 'wet and dry'). This can then be brought up to a high shine by buffing using a buffing wheel. The buffing wheel has a polishing compound which shines up the edge to a perfect finish.

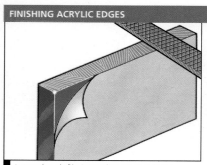

Acrylic blocks, rods, and tubes

FINISHING ACRYLIC EDGES

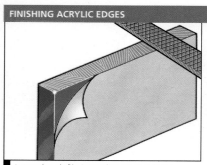
1 A metalwork file is used to remove large scratches.

2 Draw filing will improve the surface finish further.

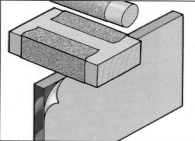
3 Silicon carbide paper can be wrapped around a suitably shaped block of wood and used to smooth down still further.

4 The mop on the buffing wheel is primed with polishing compound. The acrylic is moved in the opposite direction to the spin.

Removing surface scratches

Surface abrasions in acrylic can be removed but this takes much time and effort and they are to be avoided if at all possible. To remove them a medium grade silicon carbide abrasive is used to remove material from around the scratch. This makes the surface relatively flat again. Then finer grades of abrasive paper can be used followed by the buffing wheel as shown in the diagrams above.

Surface treatments

It is possible to add a great deal of interest to the plastic item you have made by adding colour or texture.

Acrylic can be dyed using special, rather expensive, plastic dyes. A cheaper alternative is to use standard clothes dyes. Areas which you do not want to colour can be protected using Copydex in the same way that wax is used in batik textiles.

Designs can be applied to plastics using permanent marker pens

It is also possible to paint onto plastics. A cellulose paint is used on ABS and acrylic, and enamel paints are more suitable for polystyrene.

These paints give texture as well as colour to the acrylic objects

A matt or rough texture can be applied to selected areas of acrylic and other plastics using sand blasting. In school or college workshops an alternative is to use a very fine abrasive or pumice powder. Areas to be protected are covered with adhesive tape or wax crayon.

1   Draw a flow chart of the series of tools used to 'finish' a piece of roughly shaped acrylic. Besides each box add what you would be looking for to indicate it is time to move onto the next stage.

2   Imagine you are a clock manufacturer who uses acrylic to make clock faces. Design a new face and explain, in detail, which methods your crafts people are to use to obtain the desired finish.

3   What are the health and safety issues to be considered when using a buffing wheel?

6.1 COMBINING MATERIALS

BY THE END OF THIS SPREAD, YOU SHOULD BE ABLE TO:

- understand that designers choose to combine materials using the best qualities from both

Choosing materials

In Spread 2.1 we saw how good designers understand the various qualities of materials. They use this knowledge to select the most appropriate materials for any specific task. This selection can be as basic as clear acrylic or glass for a transparent surface or as specialised as the gold engine bay insulation in the Mclaren F1 super car.

Choosing materials because of their qualities

Skis are are made from a combination of materials. Each gives the ski a particular quality which no other material can give. The main qualities a ski designer is looking for are:

- □ **Lightness** – easy to steer, comfortable to use all day, easy to carry when not being skied on.
- □ **Flexibility** – a ski has to flex along its length just the right amount to steer the skier round a turn. It must not flex across its width as the edge of the ski needs to cut into the ice.
- □ **Graphics** – needs to look good as well as being robust.
- □ **Low temperature performance** – all materials must retain qualities at the low temperature range expected.
- □ **Minimal friction** – a very tough bottom surface which accepts wax for reduction of friction, for speed.
- □ **Accepts fittings** – the bindings and ski brakes have to be attached to the ski firmly and permanently.

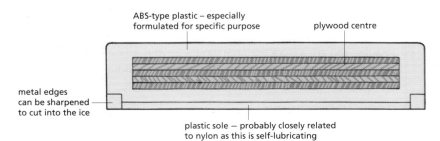

ABS-type plastic – especially formulated for specific purpose

plywood centre

metal edges can be sharpened to cut into the ice

plastic sole – probably closely related to nylon as this is self-lubricating

Simplified cross-section through a ski

Choosing materials because of their manufacturing qualities

A whole range of materials is used in the manufacture of a car like the one on the right. The thermoplastic used for the body has been chosen principally because it can be easily moulded into an intricate hollow shape. Thermoset plastic and metal are used where strength is needed, for example in the wheel mounts.

Combining materials as a coating

Probably the oldest coating used on top of another material is a wood veneer. There can be several reasons why a veneer is used.

- ☐ **Cost** – the hidden structure can be made in a much less expensive wood and a thin layer of expensive wood can be put on top.
- ☐ **Aesthetics** – veneers of different woods can be combined to produce attractive patterns. When the pieces are small the process is called *marquetry*.
- ☐ **Strength** – veneers are often chosen from woods with tight grain patterns. These resist surface damage.

A veneered desk

Another common combination involves coating ferrous metals. Ferrous metals have the strength required for many outdoor structural tasks but also have a tendency to rust. Coating in plastic overcomes this weakness and has the advantage of being available in a wide range of colours. Ferrous metals can also be coated with other non-ferrous metals to achieve the same protection, for example a galvanised finish in which iron is coated with zinc.

Plastic-coated metal

Galvanised iron

---

1 Think of two products which are made from materials which have been coated with another to improve their performance. What are they and how has their performance been improved?

2 Disassemble a torch. Identify the materials which have been used. Explain why each has been used and why they were used in that particular combination.

6.2 DISASSEMBLING FAMILIAR OBJECTS

Disassembling means taking apart. This is done to find out how things function or how they have been made. Designers sometimes use this as part of their research when given the task of improving an old design. The designer will dismantle the item and investigate each component part. This might not necessarily mean physically taking apart. The 'disassembly' of the wine glass below could be done without separating the parts. Here the glass has been divided into three components. Now it is easy to focus on the function of each part, and see how efficiently it achieves what it is designed to do. Possible improvements can be considered and further research and development can be initiated. Possible areas for investigation could include using different materials, manufacturing techniques, or the use of new technologies.

COMPONENTS		FUNCTION	ACHIEVED BY	POSSIBLE IMPROVEMENTS
Bowl		• contains liquid • allows clarity of wine to be seen • keeps white wine cool • allows red wine to breathe	• liquid-proof material/construction • clear, impurity-free material • shape gives small surface area for full glass • shape gives large surface area for half-full glass	• other liquid-proof materials • other clear materials • other insulating materials • alternative shape
Stem		• supporting the glass • stable support for bowl when held • strong support for bowl • keeps white wine cool • stable support when not held	• convenient, smooth shape • secured to centre of rotation • adequate thickness • use the stem for holding • exact location, true vertical	• alternative method of holding • use of flanges • use different material • use different colour • provide finger places • non-slip finish • shorter design
Foot		• stable support when not held • decoration/appeal	• large flat surface area • flow lines, outline	• non-slip base • coloured additives

The Dyson vacuum cleaner

This technique might well have been used by James Dyson whose Dual Cyclone vacuum cleaner has made him a household name. He realised that the design of the vacuum cleaners available in the 1980s was fundamentally flawed. The dust bag often got clogged and this reduced the efficiency of the vacuum. He designed a cleaner without a bag which he made using a unique shape and very bright colours. It is now the most popular type of vacuum outselling the nearest competition by 8 to 1.

The James Dyson cyclone system

The problem

Dissatisfied with the performance of conventional vacuum cleaners, Dyson decided to do something about it. He realised that the weak suction wasn't due to the volume of dust in the bag, but to fine dust clogging the pores of the bag and blocking the airflow. This set him on the path to a radical alternative – the world's first bagless vacuum cleaner.

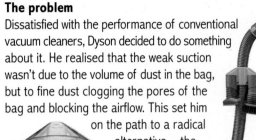

The Technology

Watching an industrial cyclone tower use centrifugal force to remove particles from the air in a spray-paint shop gave Dyson an idea – why not use the same technology in a vacuum cleaner ? He rushed home, ripped open his cleaner, and mocked up the first cyclonic model with cardboard and gaffer tape. The principle worked but it took Dyson five years and 5127 prototypes to develop a working model. In the final design, the traditional bag is replaced by two cyclone chambers. Air within these chambers spins at speeds of up to 924 mph, separating dust from air efficiently and providing 100% suction.

Components analysis

In schools and colleges we often disassemble things to see how they work and how they are made. The way that the components have been manufactured is usually quite easy to work out and can be noted down in a table as below. To find out more about these techniques you need to refer back to the spreads listed.

PART	QUANITY	MATERIAL		SHAPE		PROCESS
		General	Detail	General	Detail	
axle	2	plastic	red polythene	tube	15 mm dia. 3 mm walls 400 mm long	extruded ↓ sawn to length ↓ drilled each end
axle support	4	plastic	black nylon	bearing housing shape	15 mm dia. hole 2 mounting holes	injection moulded ↓ flash removed
wheel trim	4	metal	aluminium	circle	0.5 mm X 30 mm dia. 2 mm deep	punched/pressed from sheet ↓ deburred by machine

PARTS LIST FOR TOY CAR

see page 90
see page 82
see page 83
see page 86
see page 92
see page 64
see page 55

1 Suggest some design improvements which could be investigated for the stem part of the wine glass.

2 Choose an everyday household object and disassemble it using the same headings as those in the wine glass example.

6.3 QUALITY CONTROL

- understand quality control and quality assurance within an industrial context

A manufacturer and designer discuss a prototype

In industry 'quality' is really important. If you bought a product which did not work properly or quickly fell apart you would be unlikely to buy another. You might tell your friends not to buy one and be reluctant to purchase other products made by the same company. A reputation for poor quality would result in a company quickly going out of business.

The skilful manufacturer has to achieve consistently good quality products, quickly, and at minimal cost. A well designed product is therefore good quality and easy to make, needs little or no maintenance, and can be sold at a competitive price.

Quality assurance

To ensure that products are of a consistently high standard manufacturers are careful to involve the client in checking the product regularly so that it matches their requirements exactly. The first stage is for the client to set out a detailed **specification**. This is a list of **target qualities** which the designer and manufacturer must meet. A prototype will be produced and presented to the client and consumer so that improvements can be made before full-scale production begins. As well as checks by the clients, there is a range of independent checks and standards for companies and products. A common example of this is ISO 9001 which certificates a high level of **quality management systems** in the production company. Another common seal of quality is the British Standard (BS) Kite Mark. This shows that the product has been independently tested and meets a particular BS standard. A safe cycle helmet, for example, will display the BS Kite Mark and comply to BS 6863:89. There is more information about safety standards on page 119.

All cycle helmets must meet independent safety standards

Quality control

Having established the design requirements the factory now has to manufacture the product at the required level of quality consistently. In the past large factories would have a whole department called Quality Control. They would check the product at various stages throughout its manufacture for faults. They would often check the dimensions of components to make sure they fell within certain boundaries. These are called **tolerances**, and would be set out in the specification.

For example, a piece of 6 mm metal bar might be discarded if it was more than 0.01 mm too large or small. The tolerance would be written as 6.0 mm $\pm$ 0.01.

When a problem was identified the whole production line might be halted so the machine producing the faulty part could be recalibrated. This would cost the manufacturer time and money and was taken very seriously.

Quality checking on the iMac production line at Apple.

Process control

Today many firms have discarded the quality control department as it is not cost-effective. Operators are usually responsible for up to 10 machines at any one time. Modern machinery can often check parts of the process for quality automatically and warn operators of a drop in machine or process performance. This is called **process control**. The operator can double-check by looking closely at a recently produced sample and checking it against a test sample.

An operator of an extrusion moulder that produces CDs checks for quality.

1 How does the British Standard Kite Mark label help both manufacturers and consumers?

2 Explain the terms 'tolerance' and 'specification'.

3 Choose a product which is simple to make. Explain the measures a manufacturer might take to ensure that the highest quality is consistently achieved.

6.4 PRODUCTION STAGES

- identify the key stages of a manufacturing process
- relate these stages to an industrial situation

A student asked to design and make a simple acrylic clock has drawn out the production schedule below.

Collect a red piece of acrylic from the store	Collect a yellow piece of acrylic from the store
Mark out accurately the shape and location of the hole	Mark out accurately the shape required
Cut out shape and drill hole	Cut out shape
Heat acrylic using strip heater	Heat acrylic using strip heater
Bend over former	Bend over red acrylic

Follow safety rules when using drill

Follow safety rules when using strip heater

clamp

former

Test to see if they fit together

Collect clock and hands from the store

Glue acrylic and attach clock and hands

Check it looks attractive

Present it to the teacher for marking

The key stages in the manufacturing process are shown by the coloured backgrounds in the diagram and table. Here are examples of how the situation found in schools and colleges might compare with the much more complex situation in industry:

PRODUCTION	AT SCHOOL/COLLEGE	IN INDUSTRY
Raw materials/ transport	Students rely on the teacher to provide a selection of suitable materials.	A great deal of organisation is needed to produce and supply raw material perfect for the job, at the right quality, delivered as it is required. Industry does not store material but orders it 'just in time'.
Fabrication	Teachers supply the machinery and technicians ensure all machines are ready to use safely.	A great deal of capital may be spent on the design and installation of machinery especially made for the job. Training may be needed to ensure the workforce can keep the machines running 24 hrs a day. Marking out will not be necessary as the material will fit into a jig or other device to speed up manufacture.
Health and safety	Teachers instruct pupils on safe working practices.	Management can be prosecuted if they do not provide safe working conditions. Unions will help individual workers bringing legal procedures to gain compensation for accidents at work. External agencies are asked to inspect for safe working practices.
Assembly	Teachers advise on the best techniques/machines to use and most suitable glues.	Adhesives tested and designed especially for a specific task. Computer-aided machinery does repetitive tasks like assembly.
Components	Teachers provide pre-made components.	Components may be especially commissioned or built by another section of the company and transported in 'just in time'.
Testing for quality	Students test for accuracy at various stages during manufacture.	Quality control or process control is constant – each part must be made to comply with individual specifications and tolerances set by the commissioning firm (client).
Dispatch/ presentation to client	Present to teacher for marking – take home for use in lounge.	Various issues, such as satisfying the customer's requirements, producing the right numbers to satisfy demand, packaging and advertising, need to be considered.

1 **What is the difference between the fabrication and assembly phases of manufacture?**

2 Think of a simple project which you have completed recently. How would you adapt it so that it could be mass produced?

3 Make a list of all the machines which you have in your school/college technology department. Try to think of a project which would link these machines together in a continuous process. Explain this project using a flow chart like the one on the left.

6.5 QUALITY CONSIDERATIONS

By THE END OF THIS SPREAD, YOU SHOULD BE ABLE TO:

- define quality
- distinguish between quality of design and quality of manufacture
- understand the balance between quality and other criteria

The word 'quality' is used to describe a level of excellence. The craftsman making individual 'one-off' products will probably use quality as a selling point. Whatever the scale of production it is essential for the product to achieve an appropiate level of quality.

Manufacturers must brief designers to develop products which can be sold at a price which enables the manfacturer to make a profit and stay in business.

There are four factors which directly influence the quality of a product: design, manufacture, retail price and environmental factors. There is often what is known as a **trade-off** between these factors and quality.

Design

Designers work to quality criteria directly from an accurate specification (see Spread 1.3). If the specification is sufficiently detailed and clear then the designer can use it as a set of targets to aspire to. They may also analyse a product using a product lifestyle flow chart (described in Spread 8.1). They will try to achieve the specification in an innovative and interesting way so the artefact functions efficiently and provides a quality service but also looks good.

Lounger and stools made from specially treated beech strips

A sandwich toaster

Automatic lawn mower

A vacuum cleaner which can also be used as a table

- ☐ Do you think that these products have the balance between form and function right?
- ☐ Are they good design?
- ☐ Could they be manufactured easily?
- ☐ What price would they retail at?
- ☐ Do you think they demonstrate quality?

102

Manufacture

The next consideration will be whether it can be consistently made with the right quality. To keep the final retail price competitive a manufacturer will want to make the product from familiar and cost-effective materials, use existing machines and tools, and be built by the present workforce without retraining. The manufacturer will set the target sizes for each component – called the tolerances. They will then test the product at various stages of the manufacture to ensure that these tolerances can be achieved. Larger firms may have a quality or process control department to do this. However many firms are phasing these departments out and introducing more cost-effective ways to achieve consistently high levels of quality automatically.

Cost

In the end the judge of quality will be the consumer. If all the factors mentioned above are considered and the product can be retailed competitively, then the product will sell. It can be said to have achieved the quality required at the right price. It must be noted that it is 'quality at a price'. A similar product might be manufactured using more expensive materials giving it a longer life expectancy. However, this improvement would be reflected in the retail price. Consequently such a product is said to be aimed at a different target consumer group: one which can afford (and wants) a higher level of quality.

Environmental factors

Two important factors affect quality and design criteria: the impact on the product of environmental conditions and the impact on the environment of the product itself or its manufacturing process. Environmental pressure groups can have a large effect upon the sales of a product if they use their influence to label it 'environmentally unfriendly'. There may be several reasons for this. It could be because of an over-generous amount of wasteful packaging, or the way it works. This was the case with aerosols using CFC propellants. Most likely, though, are problems associated with disposal after the product has finished its useful life (see right). A sympathetic designer will ensure that the product either can be recycled or will biodegrade after use.

In use, the designer has to be satisfied that environmental conditions (heat, vibration, dust, etc.) will not cause degradation or malfunction of the product.

1 Explain why you think the flexible and transparent toaster is a design failure or success.

2 Give examples of two products which perform the same function but are of different quality and have correspondingly different prices.

3 Explain how a product of your choice has improved recently to overcome environmentalists' criticisms.

Dismantled, not dumped

The original Greenpeace protest on Brent Spar in 1995.

The re-use and recycling of the old oil platform 'Brent Spar' began today in the Yrkefjord on the coast of Norway. It is the end of a three year process that started with protests by Greenpeace activists and a broad public outcry in Europe against the dumping of the installation in the North Atlantic Ocean in 1995. During the protests Shell gave up its dumping plans and started a long consultation and decision-making process which resulted in a solution for re-use and recycling.

"This is a great success for the protection of the oceans and the people who supported our protests against the dumping," says Greenpeace offshore expert Jan Rispens on site in Norway. "This is the best solution in any respect: it protects the oceans, it creates jobs and reuses the material."

The most important outcome of the 'Brent Spar' protests was the decision by the environmental ministers of Europe during the OSPAR conference (Oslo-Paris Commission) in July to ban the dumping of oil and gas installations in the North Sea and the North Atlantic Ocean.

BY THE END OF THIS SPREAD, YOU SHOULD BE ABLE TO:

- understand what is meant by open and closed loop systems
- understand how feedback is used to control a system
- analyse the performance of a system to check if it is working efficiently

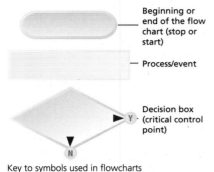

Beginning or end of the flow chart (stop or start)

Process/event

Decision box (critical control point)

Key to symbols used in flowcharts

Living at the start of the 21st century we are surrounded by 'systems'. We use transport systems to move around and security systems to protect things.

| INPUT | → | PROCESS | → | OUTPUT |

Diagram of a 'system'

Any system has three phases: input, process and output. The input is the instruction needed to operate the system. The system then processes this information and an output is produced.

This is a very simple system since the same process will take place every time the input occurs. For example, a light comes on every time you press the switch. This is called a **closed loop system**. More complex systems can sense changes in their environment and respond by altering the process to produce a more appropriate output. A system using **feedback** in this way is called an **open loop system**. For example, a security lighting system is not on all the time. It responds to movement and comes on for a short time and then goes off again. The sensing unit is producing a feedback loop and is controlling whether the light is on or off.

INPUT — PROCESS — OUTPUT

Switch on light → Electricity flows to light bulb → Bulb lights

Closed loop system

Power switched on. Sensor working but light is off.

Movement sensed. Information fed back to automatic on/off switch.

Light output on.

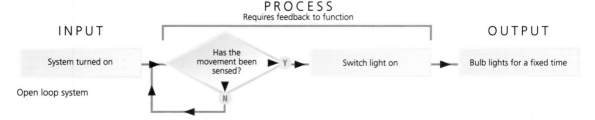

PROCESS
Requires feedback to function

INPUT — Has the movement been sensed? — Y — Switch light on — OUTPUT

System turned on — N — Bulb lights for a fixed time

Open loop system

Control systems

A modern post office sorting machine is controlled by an electronic system which reads the postcode on each letter. It then opens and shuts various gates along the track to ensure the letter reaches the right post bag. This machine is only one part, or a **subsystem**, of the whole sorting process. When the mail arrives at the sorting depot it is a mixture of letters,

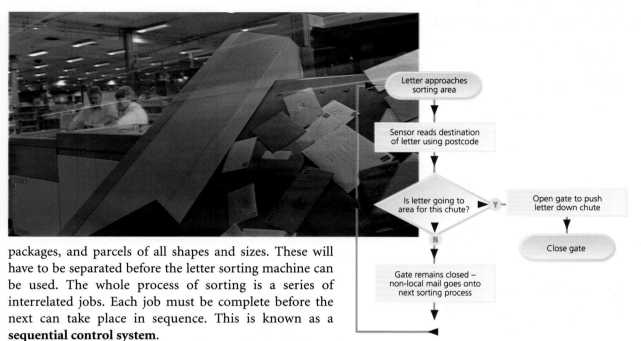

packages, and parcels of all shapes and sizes. These will have to be separated before the letter sorting machine can be used. The whole process of sorting is a series of interrelated jobs. Each job must be complete before the next can take place in sequence. This is known as a **sequential control system**.

Computer-controlled systems

Computers are often used to control complex operations. The easiest way to program the computer is to use a **flow chart**. The symbols used must be standardised.

Here you can see a flow chart used to program an automatic door at a supermarket. Notice the words Open Door and Close Door have been used to instruct the computer to read the relevant subsystem instructions.

Designers often use flow charts to analyse systems. A flow chart isolates each part of a complex system. This makes it much easier for the designer to see if the product does exactly what it was designed to do as efficiently as possible.

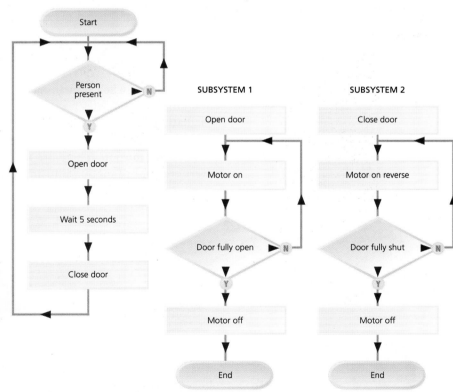

1 Choose a system you are familiar with and design a flowchart to show it.

7.2 MECHANICAL SYSTEMS

Energy conversion

The energy for the system input may come from many kinds of source including wind, water, chemical, etc. Mechanical processors include steam engines, water wheels, and electric motors. These convert the input energy into the most appropriate form to do a particular task. They can be very complex as they often combine many different mechanisms.

Types of motion

To understand how complex systems work we need to look first at the way machines can convert one type of motion to another. There are four types of motion:

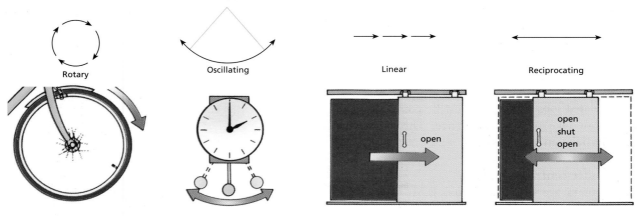

Rotary   Oscillating   Linear   Reciprocating

Rotary motion is when something spins in a circle, like a bicycle wheel. A pendulum only completes part of a circle before it changes direction. This is **oscillating motion**. **Linear motion** takes place in a straight line like a sliding door. If you constantly open and shut the door then it would be **reciprocating motion**. There are many different machines designed to convert one type of motion into another.

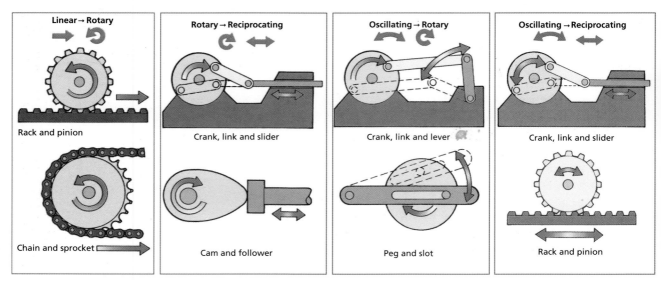

Machines for converting motions

Converting motion using cams

In the diagram the road digger is made to move up and down turning the handle at the side of the box. The *input is therefore rotary motion.* A pear-shaped piece of MDF, called a **cam**, has been fixed to the axle. When the cam turns it pushes the follower up and down, making the man rise and fall once during each turn of the handle. The *output is therefore reciprocating motion.*

Various other differently shaped cams could have been used to achieve different motion outputs (see below). If cam *D* had been used for the digger it would have dug four times for one turn of the handle.

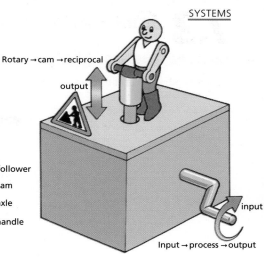

Rotary →cam →reciprocal

output

input

Input →process →output

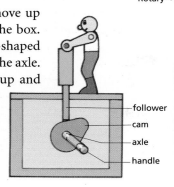

follower
cam
axle
handle

Using a cam to convert motion

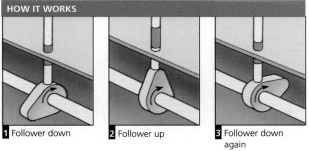

HOW IT WORKS

1 Follower down   **2** Follower up   **3** Follower down again

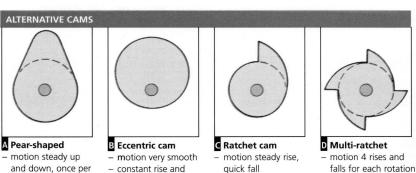

ALTERNATIVE CAMS

A Pear-shaped
– motion steady up and down, once per rotation
– no movement for 180°

B Eccentric cam
– motion very smooth
– constant rise and fall

C Ratchet cam
– motion steady rise, quick fall
– allows motion in one direction only

D Multi-ratchet
– motion 4 rises and falls for each rotation
– allows motion in one direction only

1 Describe how the digger in the example above would move if cams *B* and *C* were used.

2 Give an example (other than those used in the text) to illustrate each of the four different types of mechanical motion.

3 Draw a cube in three dimensions. Add something to the top of the box which could be made to move using one, two or three cams in a similar way to the road digger. Annotate your diagram so someone else would be able to build your device.

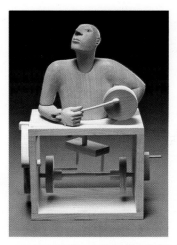

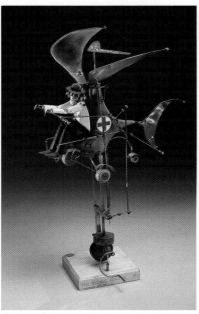

These models use machines to entertain us

7.3 GEARS

BY THE END OF THIS SPREAD, YOU SHOULD BE ABLE TO:

- describe what is meant by driver and driven gears
- increase or reduce speed using gears
- calculate speed ratios and understand the effect that this will have on the power of a machine

The diagram below shows a pair of gears. These are wheels with teeth. One wheel cannot move around without turning the other because the teeth overlap, or **mesh**.

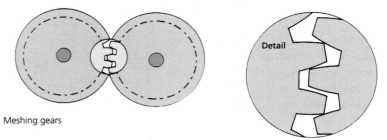

Meshing gears

If this system is to work one of these gears will be connected to a power source. This could be an electric motor which drives the rod or **shaft** through the centre of the gear. We call this gear the **driver** and the other the **driven** gear.

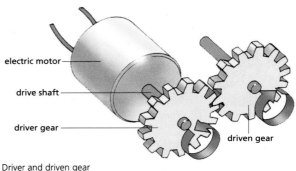

Driver and driven gear

The speed of rotation of the gears is measured in revolutions per minute (rpm).

The driven gear rotates once every two rotations of the driver gear

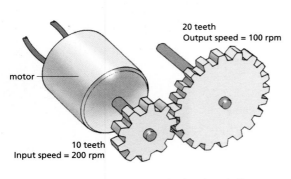

Gear ratio: slow down (1:2)

The driven gear rotates twice for every rotation of the driver gear

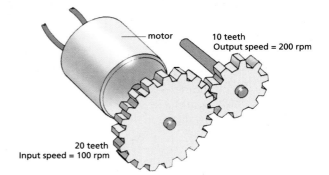

Gear ratio: speed up (2:1)

Notice how the number of teeth decide the ratio of the speeding up or slowing down. This is called the **gear ratio**. It is important to realise this will affect the power of the machine. Slower spinning gears have more power (or **torque**) than faster spinning ones.

Gear trains

If the difference between the input and output speed needs to be very large then it might not be possible to achieve this using only two gears. If more than two gears are needed then this is referred to as a **gear train**. Notice how a gear train has been used to slow down the driven gears in the diagram. The motor drives the drive shaft connected to gear A. This drives gear B at half the speed because it has double the number of teeth. C and B are on the same axle so must go at the same speed. D is driven by C. If very large numbers of gears are needed or space is limited then they might be combined.

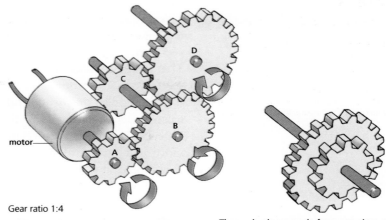

Gear ratio 1:4

	A	B	C	D
Rotation speed in rpm	100	50	50	25
Number of teeth	10	20	10	20

These wheels are made from one piece of plastic – usually nylon (could replace gears B and C).

Changing the direction of rotation

It is also important to notice the direction in which the gears turn. As the teeth mesh, gears touching each other will turn in opposite directions. If the output direction is wrong, for a particular purpose, then an extra gear might be added to change this. If this gear does not affect the output speed it is called an **idler gear**.

Special gears

Gears can also be used to change the angle between input and output. In the diagram **bevel gears** have been cut at 45 degrees. This will not alter the speed of the rotation but allows the axles to go around a right angle. A **worm gear** is like a screw thread. It has one tooth which spirals and a central shaft. This will reduce the speed of rotation between input and output rapidly. It takes one complete revolution of the worm gear to move the output gear one tooth round.

Direction of axis has moved through 90°

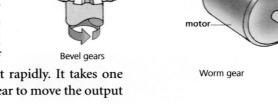

Bevel gears

Worm gear

motor

Input

Output

---

1 What is a gear called which does nothing to alter the speed of the gears? What purpose does it serve?

2 Why do we use gear trains?

3 Using only standard gears with 20, 40 or 50 teeth, design a gear train which will make the driven gear rotate at one tenth the speed of the driver gear.

7.4 LEVERS AND PULLEYS

- understand how balance is achieved in levers
- calculate the effort needed to lift different loads
- understand how pulleys work and calculate their mechanical advantage

Levers and pulleys are very simple **machines** which can help us by magnifying our muscle power.

The lever as a balance

A simple example of a lever is a see-saw. The point which supports the see-saw is called the **pivot** or **fulcrum**. Two people of the same weight will balance each other providing they sit the same distance from the fulcrum. If people are of different weights they can still balance each other if they move their position along the beam. This simple equation works out where they should sit to balance:

$$\text{Force 1} \times \text{Distance 1} = \text{Force 2} \times \text{Distance 2}$$

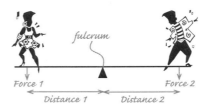

Force 1 × Distance 1 = Force 2 × Distance 2
300N × 0.5m = 300N × 0.5m
150 Nm = 150 Nm
They are in balance

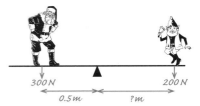

F 1 x D 1 = F 2 x D 2
300N x 0.5m = 200N x ? m
150 Nm = 200N x ? m
$\frac{150}{200}$ = ? m
= 0.75 m
The gnome should sit 0.75 m from the fulcrum

The people have a weight measured in newtons (N) and the distance from the fulcrum is measured in metres (m).

Classes (types) of lever

If we move the fulcrum to one end of an empty see-saw the only way to keep it balanced is to lift the end farthest from the fulcrum. This lift is called the **effort** (force). The force we are lifting is called the **load** (force). By adjusting the relative positions of the fulcrum, load and effort we can make various machines. These can help us in two ways. Notice how each has an advantage and disadvantage:

1. Some machines allow effort to move a long distance to move a larger load a short distance.

2. Some machines allow effort to move a short distance to move a smaller load a long distance.

Look at the diagrams to see how designers have used these qualities to build real machines.

LEVER TYPE ONE

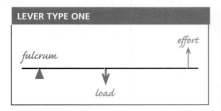

Note: the person has to lift the handle a long way up to move the load a short distance.

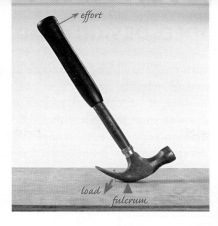

LEVER TYPE TWO

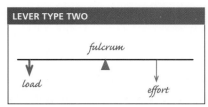

Note: the effort moves a long way pulling out the nail which only moves a small amount.

Pulleys

A *pulley* system can be used to help increase the effort of your input using a *hoist*. In the system shown below the person can only pull on the rope with 100 N of effort. The

LEVER TYPE THREE

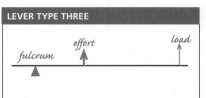

Note: the effort moves the handle a short way but the end of the rod moves a long way.

load has a weight of 200 N. The pulley system therefore needs to double the effect of the person's effort. See how the person organises the system to achieve this. By adding more pulleys heavier and heavier loads can be lifted. However, there is a disadvantage. As the weight of the load increases so does the distance through which the rope must be pulled to lift the load a set amount.

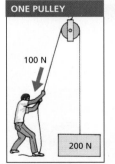

ONE PULLEY

100 N

200 N

Load does not move

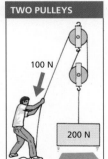

TWO PULLEYS

100 N

200 N

Load moves up

INPUT	NUMBER OF PULLEYS			
	1	2	3	4
Effort – 100 N Pull – 1 m of rope	100 N			
Max. load	100 N	200 N	300 N	400 N
Dist. load travels	1 m	0.5 m	0.33 m	0.25 m

1 Copy these see-saws onto a piece of paper. Calculate whether they are in balance or would tip clockwise or anti-clockwise. Mark this clearly next to each.

a)

b)

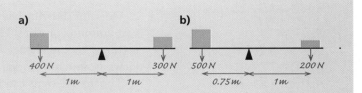

2 Think of a device, or machine, which uses levers to the benefit of its user. Explain how it works using an annotated diagram.

7.5 COMPUTER-AIDED DESIGN (CAD)

Computers are being used more and more by designers both in industry and in schools and colleges. At the beginning of the design process traditional sketching techniques are normally used because the speed of drawing must keep up with the flow of ideas. However, as soon as initial development has been completed the designer will use a computer to develop the idea. A computer has significant advantages over traditional drawing techniques.

Computer versatility

CAD (**Computer-aided design**) software allows the designer to draw any shape accurately and quickly. Standard shapes are usually scanned or stored in a library and can then be imported instantly into a drawing. Areas of the drawing can be repeated using the cut, copy and paste facilities. Components of the drawings can be moved, resized, spun or flipped into a new position. All these alterations can take place instantly and without any loss of quality. Intermediate design stages can be saved and reloaded as necessary as well as the final version. Storing the work safely is a great advantage. A floppy disc is much more convenient to transport than drawings and is much less prone to damage, or the work can be sent electronically.

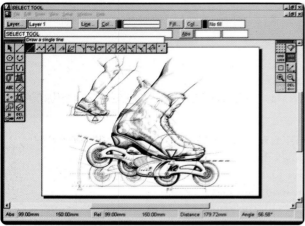

A 2-D design 'sketch'

A 3-D projection of a car

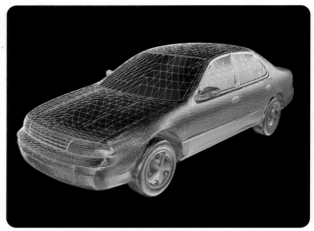

The car body is shown as a wire frame in this image

Once the drawing has been completed the computer really starts to save vast amounts of time. The designer can try different colours, shades and textures. He can change a 2-dimensional image into 3-D and even display views around or through what he has drawn to see it from different angles.

The final designs can be printed without any loss of quality. **Parts lists** can be generated by computer if needed. The design information is in a state which can be loaded onto other computers anywhere in the world. **Video conferencing** even allows designers sitting at different computers to develop the same design on screen. They can talk over the design and even take over the mouse control to illustrate their ideas. The design can then be sent to other computers which will control the actual manufacture of the artefact without any need for redrawing (see next spread).

Computer modelling and testing

As computers become more powerful they are able to test and trial ideas by simulating the environment in which they will be used. It is possible to design a mechanism, an electronic circuit or even an entire room interior and then see if it will function properly. Ergonomic information can be checked to ensure that the product is easy to use. It is possible to simulate loads and predict the stresses that different parts of the structure might be exposed to. This is a much more cost-effective way to test products – especially ones which are to be used in unusual or dangerous environments like space, for example.

Marketing and publicity

Some of the drawings and models, together with descriptive text and test reports, will be suitable for designing **data sheets** and **publicity material**. Graphics can be copied into desktop publishing packages and full use made of colour for a variety of brochures and advertising literature related to products you have designed.

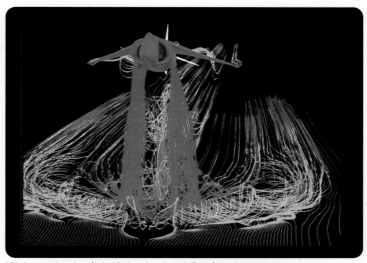

This is a Harrier aircraft simulation showing air flow from the engine

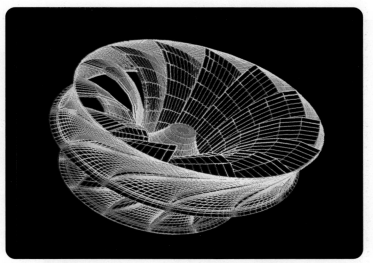

This shows the pressures on a jet engine compressor (blue is low pressure and red is high pressure)

---

1 Use a pencil and paper to draw the best CD storage system you can in three minutes. Now time how long it takes to do the same drawing using a computer. Explain which was the quickest method, and then which was the best.

2 List the advantages of using a computer to design a new light shade.

3 Think of a product which is likely to be used in an environment which would be difficult to recreate in any other way than on a computer. Explain what the product is and what tests you would ask the computer to perform.

7.6 COMPUTER-AIDED MANUFACTURE (CAM)

BY THE END OF THIS SPREAD, YOU SHOULD BE ABLE TO:

- suggest an appropriate use for CAM
- identify the main advantages and disadvantages of using CAM during one of your projects
- discuss the merits of CAM when compared against manual manufacturing techniques

In the previous spread we saw how computers could be used to help designers to develop and present their ideas. Computers can also be used to replace machine operators by carrying out a number of tasks more effectively. When a computer controls a machine to make something we call this **computer-aided manufacture** or CAM. The results of CAD can be fed straight into a CAM system.

Using CAM at school or college

In a school workshop you may find a computer-controlled router like the one pictured. This machine can cut most light materials very accurately and quickly. You use it to make a circle from a piece of acrylic. You draw the circle on the computer and then let the computer control the router to cut the shape. Providing you know how to use the software then the job could be completed very quickly. Without this machine the task would be a real test of craftsmanship. It would certainly take longer to make and be very difficult to produce a perfect circle.

Small computer controlled router

CAM in a car plant

Using CAM in industry

The jobs which make up the manufacturing process in industry are much more complex. A CAM system can be used to control many tasks simultaneously. In the picture you can see car parts being welded together using computer-controlled robot arms. Vast numbers of identical products are being made – this is called **mass production**. There are advantages and disadvantages that need to be considered when deciding whether to install such a system in a factory. The equipment is very expensive and complicated to set up so the installation costs will be very high. You may well need very skilled employees to set up this system. However, once the system is running the computer will control most or all of the machinery. The task will be completed very accurately, safely and quickly, and could continue for long periods without losing quality.

Furniture manufacturers can also benefit from using a CAM system even though they do not make vast numbers of identical products. They may have a product range from which people choose a particular style. They would use a computer which can store details of the various styles and allow them to make a small number of chairs in one style and then quickly switch to aother style. CAM is therefore useful for this **batch production** as well. This is called **flexible manufacturing**.

CAM may even be advantageous for a company who has to produce single items, like a sign writer. This is called **one-off production**. The computer can have many typefaces stored in its memory which can be arranged easily on screen to suit the customer's requirements. The computer can then control the machine which cuts out the letters to make the sign.

Computer-aided sign writing

COMPARISON BETWEEN CAM AND MANUAL MANUFACTURING PROCESSES

CAM	Manual manufacture
• Particularly accurate, producing items identical to each other, at high speed.	• Can be accurate if person is highly trained; no two items would be identical; long production time.
• Production system can go on for long periods without resting or getting bored.	• Person has legal time limits within which to work; quality and safety may be compromised as they get tired.
• Can work safely without risk of injury, no matter how heavy, delicate or dangerous the materials being used.	• Health and safety regulations need to be followed to ensure safe working practices; it might not be possible to work with some very heavy, delicate or dangerous materials.
• Risk of low utilisation or obsolescence.	• Labour-intensive, high running costs.
• Installation and initial programming very costly and highly skilled, but running costs and skill factors low once in production (except for maintenance).	• Lower installation cost and quicker to get production started.

1 Why would we use CAM to make a large number of identical items?

2 Explain why you might make a product using hand tools rather than a CAM system.

3 Explain why there are fewer injuries when a CAM system is being used rather than a manual manufacturing process.

7.7 DESIGNING CONTROL SYSTEMS

BY THE END OF THIS SPREAD, YOU SHOULD BE ABLE TO:

- identify a range of control systems to achieve a given output from a given input
- choose the most appropriate control system for your project

Many major GCSE projects do not include any control systems although those which do can be more interesting and innovative. The types of control (which need to be simple to build because of the time constraints) fall into three categories: electronic – mechanical – pneumatic.

Electronic systems

One very versatile example of an electronic control is the Darlington pair sensing circuit. This is a relatively simple circuit to build and can be used in many ways. Essentially it is a transistorised processor which can sense changes in light, pressure, heat or moisture and amplify tiny changes into large control or warning signals. The circuit indicates that it has sensed an input by switching on a variety of outputs. These could be a bulb, LED (light-emitting diode), a buzzer or even a switch for an electric motor .

A Darlington pair used as a light meter for cricket matches

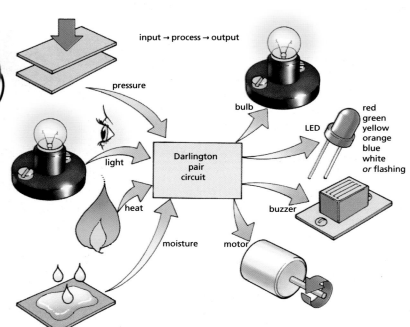

input → process → output

bulb

LED

red
green
yellow
orange
blue
white
or flashing

pressure

light

Darlington pair circuit

heat

moisture

buzzer

motor

Some of the uses of a Darlington pair sensing circuit

Mechanical systems

The information on Spread 7.2 shows a variety of mechanisms which can convert one sort of motion to another. Once you have established the input motion and output motion required you can use this information to find a suitable mechanism which will achieve this. Various gears, linkages or cams can be used to convert an input into one or more outputs.

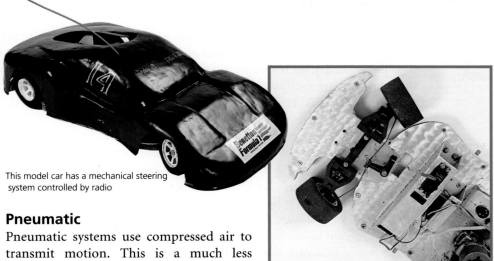

This model car has a mechanical steering system controlled by radio

Pneumatic

Pneumatic systems use compressed air to transmit motion. This is a much less common control system simply because many schools and colleges cannot afford the equipment needed. Devices used for GCSE projects therefore tend to be very simple systems using easily found equipment. Using flexible tubes to transmit the power gives a pneumatic system advantages over a mechanical one. The input and output motions can be a long way apart, or connected using a complex route.

Choosing the right system

If the specification of the project is written clearly and accurately and is quantifiable, the designer knows precisely what is required and the limits within which he or she must work. Using this information the inputs and outputs required can be established. A little modelling and testing should soon indicate the best solution to a control problem.

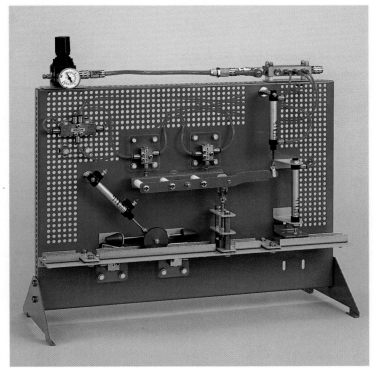

A pneumatic control display

---

1 Explain one control system which a designer could use to open a small box by pushing a button on the front. Use a diagram to help you show how this might work.

2 Plan how to use a Darlington pair amplifier to control a household appliance. Use annotated diagrams to explain your idea. Explain clearly the system in terms of:
Input → Processor → Output.

8.1 RECOGNISING HAZARDS IN PRODUCTS

- analyse a product for potential hazards
- identify safety symbols on products

When we buy a product we expect it to do what it was built for without any problems. If it doesn't work or is awkward to use then we return it. If it causes an injury we blame the manufacturer and in serious cases take them to court for compensation. This rarely happens because designers and manufacturers make every effort to design a product to work efficiently and safely.

Systematic analysis for potential hazards

To achieve this designers use a method of analysing existing products using a flow chart of the product's lifestyle. This allows them to look closely at the ways the product is likely to be used. They can focus in on potential hazards and suggest ways of minimising the risk.

The diagram below shows the **lifestyle flow diagram** for an electric kettle. Notice how each stage is analysed for potential hazards and then a solution has been suggested.

The level of water inside the kettle needs to be clearly displayed – this would minimise the chance of turning on an empty kettle which might burn out the element.

An automatic method of disconnecting the electrical supply when the kettle is lifted avoids the potential danger of water coming into contact with the electricity supply.

Need for boiling water to make a hot drink

Has the kettle enough water in it? — N → Take kettle to water supply, add water.

Y

Switch on kettle

This might be done with a wet finger; the switch housing should be water proof.

If there is no indication of how hot the water is inside, the impatient operator might be tempted to test the side of the kettle to see if it is working – is it insulated?

Wait until kettle has boiled the water

Has the kettle boiled the water? — N

Y

Automatic switch off or manual

Non-automatic kettles need some warning that the heating process needs to be switched off.

Weight of water can be significant, especialy for older people who might have weak wrists. This can be amplified if the handle is placed on the side since the kettle tends to want to rotate.

1. Pick up kettle
2. Tip out boiling water into container

The positioning of the handle needs to be carefully thought out. When the kettle is tipped up the steam must not be able to burn the operator's hand.

Spout needs to be carefully designed so that the pouring is efficient and does not spill.

Having analysed existing products in a similar way the designer will try to use this knowledge to produce a safer product. The prototype will be tested for safety by the manufacturer, including electrical insulation. They will consider all the different people who might use it and the varying requirements they might have under varying environmental conditions.

When the makers are happy that the product is safe, independent safety inspectors are asked to test it. To show the consumer that the product has passed the safety tests a series of symbols are printed on the package.

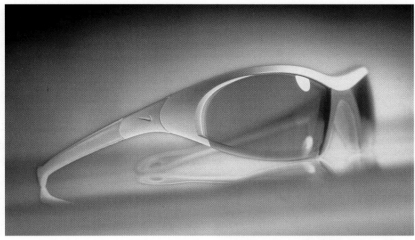

These sunglasses are designed for use by athletes. The lenses wrap around the edge of the head to ensure that athletes can see what's happening on either side of them to avoid collisions.

BS Kite Mark

The British Standard Kite Mark shows that the product has been independently tested and comes up to the standard expected by the British Standards Institute.

CE Mark

The European Commission has set down a series of safety requirements. This mark shows that the manufacturer thinks they have achieved these standards.

Embossed triangle

This triangle is slightly raised so that blind people are warned that the contents may have some danger to them. It is a **tactile** danger warning.

BEAB Mark

This mark shows that both the product and the manufacturing process have been passed by the British Electrotechnical Approvals Board for electrical safety.

1 List the potential safety hazards of a toy designed for a very young child.

2 Draw a lifestyle analysis flow chart for a craft knife. Suggest ways the design could be improved to make it safer and easier to use.

3 Design a package for a potentially very hazardous household product. Ensure your design has all the necessary safety warnings.

8.2 SAFETY AT WORK

BY THE END OF THIS SPREAD, YOU SHOULD BE ABLE TO:

- understand the safety issues in a school or college workshop
- identify safety procedures in an industrial location

Every time your teacher shows you how to use a new machine they will point out the safety rules. They have to do this by law, so that you have the information you need to work safely. Teachers tend to be very good at explaining things and therefore there are very few accidents in school and college workshops.

Your safety depends upon your teacher, the school technician, inspectors and *you*. Teachers control the environment in which you work and set up the working procedures which you follow. They also select the materials and ensure that you wear the right safety equipment. The technician has to maintain both the machinery and tools to keep them in good order and properly adjusted. Every year an inspector will ensure that everything is safe and will recommend improvements or additional maintenance if things are becoming dangerous due to age. If all these procedures have been followed properly then the responsibility for safety lies with the operator who must be prepared and follow the rules properly.

The key factors in safe working practices in workshops are shown in the diagram below. Your teacher will have used a chart like this to set out all the potential safety hazards and the procedures used to avoid accidents. This is called a **risk assessment**.

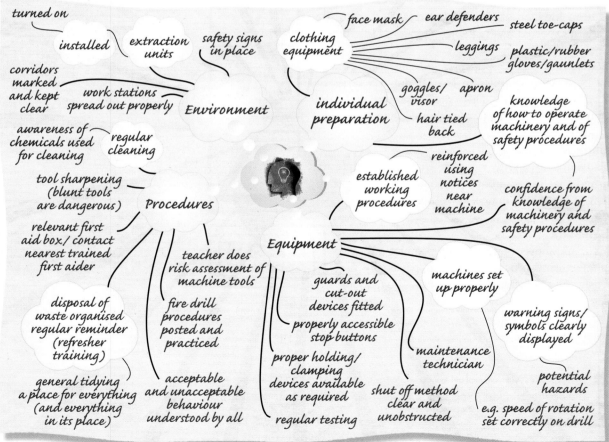

Health/safety in a school or college workshop

The **Health and Safety at Work Act (1974)** ensures that factories are set up to be safe places to work in. They are regularly inspected by the Health and Safety Executive inspectors who will take employers who do not meet the regulations to court.

If you visit a factory you may well see a poster like the one opposite which sets out the safety contract between the employer and the employee. Other things to look for include all the stickers used to indicate various potential hazards. These stickers use a standard system of symbols on three different coloured backgrounds.

- Red signs show things which are not allowed.
- Blue signs shows things which must be done.
- Yellow signs are warnings.

In the picture on the right there are yellow lines on the factory floor. These indicate areas which must be kept clear of obstruction. This is to allow the people with lifting devices and materials to move safely around the factory floor. The areas are also kept clear to aid escape in case of emergencies like fire.

If you do visit a factory look for ways in which the machines are designed to be operated safely. After putting a new piece of material into a machine the operator often has to close a door or move away to start the machine working. The machine will not do the job unless the safety screen is closed. There may also be other back-up (fail-safe) systems which will stop the machine if something unexpected happens.

Note: Health and Safety literature may be obtained from RS Components Ltd.

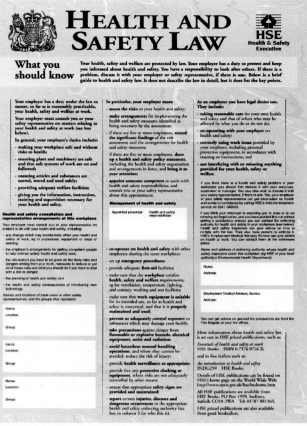

Health and Safety contract poster from HMSO

The safety corridor is clearly marked with yellow lines

1 What is the difference between a blue sign and a red sign?

2 Look around your workshop and identify the safety stickers and what they are for.

3 Choose a machine tool and use the chart opposite to identify all the safety issues.

APPENDIX 1 – ERGONOMIC DATA

One essential element for a good quality design is that it is easy and comfortable to use. The product has been carefully designed to fit the human anatomy perfectly. Such products are **ergonomically designed**.

There are many factors which could be taken into account to make a product ergonomically more efficient. Designers are constantly using new technology to improve existing products by making them easier to use. We only have to look at the development of any household products over the years to see how designers have become increasingly **ergonomically sensitive**.

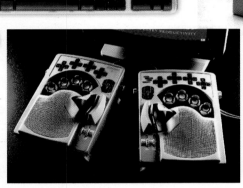

Designers have focused on keyboard design to ease keying and reduce strain

How to sit at a computer

Adjust monitor height so top of screen is below horizontal line of sight

Position monitor 20–24 inches away from eyes

Adjust seat height so upper arms hang vertically, elbows bent at 90°

Hold wrists in neutral position not bent upward or downward

Adjust backrest to support the small of the back

Use a document holder next to the screen, rather than laying papers flat

Use a footrest, if necessary, to adjust for height

Average sizes of people

Designers use **anthropometric data** to ensure the things they design are the right size. Anthroprometric data are average measurements of all parts of the body taken from a very large number (population) of people. This allows us to suggest things such as 'normal' height for six-year-old girls, or head size for fifteen-year-old boys.

A designer will normally reject the bottom 5% and the top 5% of the population sample. The design will then be appropriate for 90% of the population. Someone might be designing a chair for middle-aged women, for example. They would probably use many pieces of information like the width of the hips, to ensure that the seat is the right width. For this, they would be given the following information:

5%	50%	95% of population
under 320 mm	under 375 mm	under 430 mm

As a result they would make the chair seat width to accommodate hips of between 320 and 430 mm.

The tables below show a selection of data useful for GCSE projects.

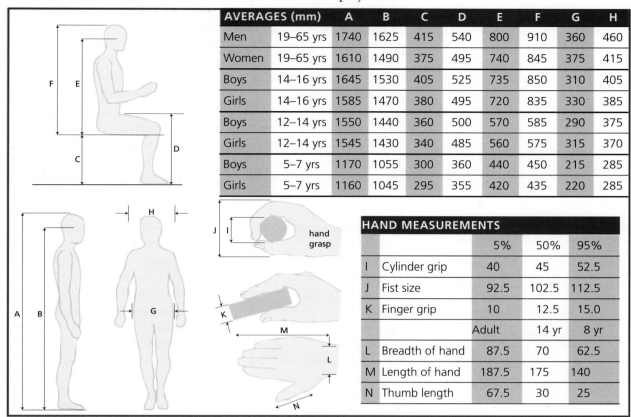

AVERAGES (mm)		A	B	C	D	E	F	G	H
Men	19–65 yrs	1740	1625	415	540	800	910	360	460
Women	19–65 yrs	1610	1490	375	495	740	845	375	415
Boys	14–16 yrs	1645	1530	405	525	735	850	310	405
Girls	14–16 yrs	1585	1470	380	495	720	835	330	385
Boys	12–14 yrs	1550	1440	360	500	570	585	290	375
Girls	12–14 yrs	1545	1430	340	485	560	575	315	370
Boys	5–7 yrs	1170	1055	300	360	440	450	215	285
Girls	5–7 yrs	1160	1045	295	355	420	435	220	285

hand grasp

HAND MEASUREMENTS		5%	50%	95%
I	Cylinder grip	40	45	52.5
J	Fist size	92.5	102.5	112.5
K	Finger grip	10	12.5	15.0
		Adult	14 yr	8 yr
L	Breadth of hand	87.5	70	62.5
M	Length of hand	187.5	175	140
N	Thumb length	67.5	30	25

Standard sizes of products

Another factor related to ease of use is the adoption of standard parts and sizes. There are a few standard sizes around. If your project involves using components like batteries or CDs then the following table sizes will be an important part of the data collection for your project. (L, W, D stand for Length, Width, and Depth.)

	L	W	D		L	W	D
CD	120	120	1.5	Battery holders			
CD cases	142	124	9	4HP7 or 4AA	111	25	16
Audio tapes	100	64	13	2HP11 or 2C	64	56	24
Audio tape cases	109	70	17	4HP11 or 4C	110	54	24
Floppy disc	94	94	4	6HP7 or 6AA	61	45	28
Floppy disc cases	98	96	8	2HP2 or 2D	70	71	27
Video	188	103	24	4HP2 or 4D	140	71	27
Video box	204	120	30	2HP7 or 2AA	59	25	15
Sega games box	177	127	27	Pencils	180	8	8
A4 paper	297	210	various	Kitchen roll	300	23	23
A3 paper	410	297	various	Medium eggs	55	40	40
Maps	250	150	various	bottles	110	40	40
Single mattress	1900	950	various	75 cl wine bottle	275	74	74
Double mattress	1900	1350	various	Toast thick	140	120	12.5
King size mattress	1980	1500	various	Toast thin	140	120	10

Glossary

aesthetics: concerning the beauty of an object or product. What makes a product visually appealing.

adhesive: a substance used to stick materials together.

annealing: a heat treatment for toughening metals where you heat the metal and allow it to cool slowly.

anthropometrics: the scientific study of the measurements of the human body.

bending: when a material deflects under a force.

burr: the edge of a metal that is often removed by filing (unless it is a cutting tool).

CAD: computer-aided design.

CAM: computer-aided manufacture.

carcase: the skeleton or framework of an object.

casting: shaping molten metal by pouring it into a mould.

chamfer: a small angle that is shaped onto the edge of a material to take off the sharp corner or to visually soften the edge.

composite: a material that is made up of various parts, often layers, for example a carbon-fibre shell on a racing car.

component: part of a product that is assembled to make a larger product. For example, a bicycle is made from a frame with many components assembled on to it.

compression: the squeezing force exerted on a material.

conductivity: a measure of the ability of a material to conduct heat or electricity.

criteria: standards used to judge something. For example, design criteria might be appearance, ease of use, safety, comfort, etc.

durability: a measure of the ability of a product to be long lasting or hardwearing.

die: a device for stamping, cutting or moulding a material into a particular shape.

draft angle: the angle that is put onto moulds when forming plastics and casting metals to ensure easy extraction of the mould after working.

ergonomics: the study of the efficiency of people in their working environment. Working environment relates to whenever a person uses an object, not just 'at work'.

elasticity: the property of certain materials that enables them to return to their original dimensions after an applied load has been removed.

extraction: a safety process that sucks unwanted dusts and fumes from the air.

fabrication: construction or manufacture from prepared components.

form: the visual appearance or shape of a product.

function: how a product works, operates or fulfils its purpose.

hardness: describes the ability of a material to withstand scratching or denting.

injection mould: a method of forming plastics by heating up granules of plastic and then injecting the molten plastic into a mould.

jig: a device that holds a piece of work and may guide the tools operating on it.

knock-down-fitting: a joining device that enables a product to be assembled and taken apart again easily, often with simple tools.

laminate: to manufacture by placing layer on layer.

manufacture: to make or produce a product.

monocoque: a structure where the chassis is an integral part of the body.

orthographic: a drawing system where the projection lines are parallel. A method of looking at a product from different elevations, for example: front elevation, end elevation and plan elevation.

pilot hole: a small-diameter hole drilled before drilling a larger hole or as a guide for a wood screw or metal screw thread.

reliability: a measure of a product's ability to be of consistent quality throughout its life.

scribe: to mark with a pointed tool.

strength: the ability of a material to withstand being damaged.

stress: tensile stress and compressive stress are forces applied to a body that tend either to extend it or compress it.

strain: the linear strain or tensile strain is the ratio of the change in length to the original length of a material.

toughness: a measure of the ability of a material to withstand a shock load.

tempering: after a metal has been hardened it will often be tempered to take some of the brittleness away.

template: a thin piece of board or metal that is used as a guide for marking out or cutting a material.

tension: the stretching force exerted on a material.

vacuum forming: a method of forming plastics by heating sheet plastic and then forming the plastic over the mould by extracting the air from underneath the mould.

veneer: a thin covering of fine wood or other surface material applied to a coarser or inferior grade wood or to a manufactured board.

Index

A
abrasives 52
ABS 81
acrylic 80–84
adhesives
    wood 48
    metal 68
    plastics 88–89
aluminium 54
aluminium oxide paper 52
analysis 6
annealing 55, 76
annotation 12
anthropometrics 122–123
attributes analysis 13

B
bandsaw 37
bench drill 59
bending
    metals 63
    plastics 84
bevel gears 109
bolt 69
bow 30
brace and bit 35
bradawl 33
brainstorm 6
brass 54
brazing 68, 73
bridle joint 44 45
brief 6–7
burrs
butt joint 42, 44–46

C
CAD 112–113
calendering 91
CAM 114–115
cams 107
carcase 42
carving wood 38
casting
    metals 67
    plastics 87
centre punch 56
chain 106
checking 104–105
coating 79, 95
chisels 34
components analysis 97
compression moulding 91
computer-aided design 112–113
computer-aided manufacture 114–115
control systems 116–117
cope 67
copper 54

D
Darlington pair 116

datum 56
depth stop 59
design
    brief 6–7
    development 14
    evaluation 13
    ideas 12–13
die-casting 64–65
die, threading 70
dip coating 79
disassembly 96–97
dividers 57
dovetail joint 42, 44–45
draft angle 67
drag 67
draw filing 62
dust extraction 36–37
Dyson, James 96–97

E
enamelling 79
environment 8
epoxy resin 80
ergonomics 122–123
evaluation 24
exploded drawing 19
extrusion 90

F
feedback
    control 104
    user 21
ferrous 54
files 62
finger joint 42
finishing 52–53, 78, 92
fitness for purpose 14
flexible manufacturing 115
flux 72
folding
    bars 63
    machine 63
forging 66
fork 38
form 14
forming metals 63
framework 42, 44–45
framework joints 44–45
fulcrum 110
function 15

G
galvanised 95
gears
    driver and driven 108
    ratio 108
    train 109
glasspaper 52
glues 48
gouges 38
GRP 87

grub screw 69
guillotine 58

H
hacksaw 58
halving joint 44
hand drill 35
hand vice 59
hardening 76
hardwoods 30–31
haunch 45
hazards 118–119
heartwood 30
heat treatment 76–77
high-impact polystyrene 80
high speed steel 54
hinges 49
HIPS 80
housing joint 43
hygroscopic 32

I
idler gear 109
injection moulding 86,90
input 104
interview 9

J
jigs 20,33, 50–51
jigsaw 36

K
kerfs 40
knock-down fittings 49

L
laminating 40
lathe
    metal 60
    tools 60
    wood 38
levers 110–111
linear motion 106
loop
    closed 104
    open 104

M
machine power tools 37
machine vice 59
manufactured boards 30–31, 43
manufacturing in quantity 20, 50, 74, 90, 114
market 8
marking knife 33
marking out 32-33
mass production 114
materials
    choosing 15
    combining 94–95
    testing 28

MDF 31
mechanical advantage 111
medium-density fibreboard 31
metals
    bending 63
    casting 67
    choosing 54
    cutting and drilling 58–59
    finishing 78–79
    forging 66
    heat treatment 76
    joining 15, 66–69, 72–73
    marking out 56-57
    polishing 55, 78
    preparing 54–55
    pressing 64
    shaping/forming 15, 62–63
    threading and riveting 70–71
    turning and milling 60–61
mild steel 54
milling 61
mitre joint 42, 44, 46
modelling 16–17
modelling materials 17
moisture content 30
mole grip 59
mood board 9
mortise
    cutter 37
    joints 43-46
motion
    converting 107
    types 106

N
nails 49
need 6
needle files 62
non-ferrous 54
nuts 69
nylon 80

O
odd-leg callipers 57
oscillating 106
output 104

P
panels 47
PAR 32
parts list 97
pattern 67
permanent/semi-permanent fixing 89
PET 81
phenol formaldehyde 80
piercing saw 58
pillar drill 59
pivot 110
planer 37
planes
    types 35
    using 39

planning schedule 22
plastic
    choosing 80
    coating 79
    cutting 82–83
    finishing 92–93
    joining 15, 88–89
    marking out 81
    shaping/forming 15, 84–87
pneumatics 117
polyester 80
polyethylene 81
polypropylene 81
polystyrene 80
polythene 80
power tools 36
press forming
    plastics 84
    metals 64
process 104
process control 99
production 100–101
projections
    isometric 18
    oblique 18
    orthographic 18
    perspective 18
prototype 21, 29
PSE 32
pulleys 111
PVC 81

Q
quality
    assurance 98
    considerations 102–103
    control 98–99
    management 98
questionnaire 8

R
rack and pinion 106
radial arm saw 37
rebate
    joint 42
    plane 35
reciprocating 106
rendering 18
research 8
riser 67
risk assessment 120
rivets 68, 71
rotary motion 106
rotational moulding 91
router 36, 50
runner 67

S
safety 118-121
sander power 36
sapwood 30
sash cramps 48

saws
    metal 58
    wood 34
screws 49
scriber 56
seasoning 30
shooting board 39
softwoods 30–31
soldering 68, 72
specification 10–11
sprocket 106
square
    engineers 56
    try 32
stainless steels 54
steam bending 40
steels 54
stud 69
surface
    gauge 57
    plate 57
systems and control 104–105
systems
    computer controlled 105
    control 104–105, 116–117
    mechanical 106

T
taps 70
tempering 76–77
templates 20, 50-51, 74–75
thermoplastics 80
thermosetting 80
threads 70
tin snips 58
titanium 54
tolerances 98–99
tongue and groove 47

U
urea formaldehyde 80
user trials 25

V
vacuum forming 85
vee block 57
veneers 41
video conferencing 112

W
washers 69
wood
    adhesives 48
    bending 40–41
    finishing 52–53
    joining 15, 42–49
    shaping 115, 39
    split 30
    twist 30
    warp 30, 46
working drawing 19
worm gear 109

Acknowledgements

The publisher would like to thank the following for their kind permission to reproduce the following photographs:

Cover and Title page Telegraph Colour Library; p. 7 Stockfile/Steven Behr; p. 10 courtesy (above) Apple Computer Inc. and (centre) K2 (UK) Ltd., (below) Stockfile/Steven Behr; p. 11 all photos courtesy K2; pp. 21–25 all photos Ben Wilson; p. 26 Nutcracker by Christian Marx, Brainbox/Key Industrial Equipment Ltd., Juicy Salif by Philippe Starck, Alessi/Contemporary Designs Ltd., Andrew Varah Furniture Designer/Paul Lapsley, Sugar Bowl by Michael Graves, Alessi/Key Industrial Equipment Ltd., Freeplay Wind Up Radio by Trevor Baylis/BayGen Freeplay Energy Europe Ltd.; p. 27 Hannibal tape dispenser, Attila can presser both by Julian Brown, Rexite/Key Industrial Equipment Ltd.; p. 29 (above) courtesy Jaguar Cars Ltd., (below) Image Bank/Didier Charre; p. 31 courtesy Hindleys Educational Supplies; p. 33 courtesy Trend Machinery & Cutting Tools Ltd.; p. 34 courtesy Spear & Jackson, Crown Hand Tools Ltd. and Record Hand Tools Ltd.; p. 35 courtesy Record Hand Tools Ltd. and Stanley Europe; p. 36 courtesy of Axminster Power Tools and Trend Machinery & Cutting Tools Ltd.; p. 37 courtesy Draper Tools Ltd. and Record Power Tools Ltd.; p. 38 (above) ACE Photo Agency/Mauritius, courtesy (below) Draper Tools Ltd.; p. 39 courtesy Record Hand Tools Ltd.; p. 40 (centre) Christie's Images, (below) Jyri Kermik; p. 41 Christie's Images; pp. 44 and 48 courtesy Record Hand Tools Ltd.; p. 50 courtesy Trend Machinery & Cutting Tools Ltd.; p. 51 courtesy Parker Knoll; p. 51 (above) Christie's Images, courtesy (above centre) Julian Chichester Designs Ltd. and (centre) British Toymaker's Guild/Heartwood, (below centre) ACE Photo Agency/Peter Adams, (below) Houses & Interiors/Simon Butcher; p. 54 (left and centre) courtesy Hindleys Educational Supplies, (right) Leslie Garland Picture Library; pp. 56–57 courtesy of Record Hand Tools Ltd. and Draper Tools Ltd.; p. 58 (above) Leslie Garland Picture Library/E. Ryle Hodges, (from top) courtesy Draper Tools Ltd., Technology Enhancement Programme (TEP) and Spear & Jackson; p. 59 courtesy Draper Tools Ltd.; p. 61 (above) courtesy Draper Tools Ltd., (below) ACE Photo Agency/Mugshots; p. 62 courtesy Draper Tools Ltd.; p. 64 (left) Science Photo Library/Pascal Nieto, Jerrican, courtesy (right) Rover Group and (below left) Dualit Ltd.; p. 65 (top) courtesy Lledo Plc, (centre) Leslie Garland Picture Library; p. 70–71 all courtesy Draper Tools Ltd.; p. 72 courtesy (above) Draper Tools Ltd. and (below) Rapid Electronics Ltd.; p. 76 courtesy (above) Draper Tools Ltd. and (below) Stanley Europe; p. 77 courtesy Raleigh Industries Ltd.; p. 78 courtesy (above and centre) 3M Ltd. and (below) Hammerite Products Ltd.; p. 80 courtesy Caradon MK Electric UK; p. 82 courtesy Hindleys Educational Supplies; p. 83 courtesy Draper Tools Ltd.; p. 87 courtesy Educational & Scientific Products Ltd.; p. 89 courtesy Harrison Silverdale Ltd. and Trylon Ltd.; p. 90 courtesy (above) Boston Matthews and (below) RPC Containers Ltd.; p. 91 (above) Image Bank/HMS Images, courtesy (centre) Excelsior Group International and (below) Tefal UK Ltd.; p. 92 courtesy Hindleys Educational Supplies; p. 93 courtesy (above) Edding UK Ltd. and (below) Inscribe Ltd.; p. 94 (left) courtesy Nitro Snowboards, (right) ACE Photo Agency/Geoff Smyth; p. 95 (above) Collections/Anthea Sieveking, (above centre) Christie's Images, (below centre) Leslie Garland Picture Library, (below) courtesy Haws Watering Cans Ltd.; p. 97 courtesy Dyson Appliances Ltd.; p. 98 Image Bank/S. Dunwell; p. 99 (above and centre) courtesy of Apple Computer Inc., (below) Science Photo Library/Maximilian Stock; p. 102 Robomow/Friendly Machines UK Ltd., Woven Chair/Lee Ackland, Toaster/Nora Brelo, Sheffield Hallam University, RSA Student Design Award Winner 1997/8, Vacuum Cleaner/Scott Chapps, Ravensbourne College of Design & Communication, RSA Student Design Award Winner 1997/8; p. 103 Greenpeace/Thompson; p. 105 The Post Office Photographic Library; p. 107 Cabaret Mechanical Theatre/Heini Schneebeli; p. 110 Photos Horticultural; p. 111 (right) Mike Helliwell; p. 112 courtesy (above and centre left) K2 (UK) Ltd and Techsoft UK Ltd. (centre right) Science Photo Library/Alfred Pasieka; p. 113 all photos Science Photo Library (above) NASA AMES Research Centre, (below) Rosenfield Images Ltd.; p. 114 (above) courtesy Techsoft UK Ltd., (below) Leslie Garland Picture Library/E. Ryle-Hodges; p. 115 courtesy Spandex Plc; p. 117 courtesy Nicholl Education Ltd.; p. 119 courtesy IDEO; p. 121 (above) Crown copyright material is reproduced with the permission of the Controller of Her Majesty's Stationery Office, (below) Leslie Garland Picture Library.

Additional photography by Martin Sookias

Illustrations by Nick Hawken

Special thanks to St Augustine's Upper School, Oxford, Warlands Cycles and Ben Wilson